Editor
Lorin E. Klistoff, M.A.

Managing Editor
Karen Goldfluss, M.S. Ed.

Editor-in-Chief
Sharon Coan, M.S. Ed.

Illustrator
Kevin Barnes
Alexandra Artigas

Cover Artist
Brenda DiAntonis

Art Coordinator
Kevin Barnes

Art Director
CJae Froshay

Imaging
Ralph Olmedo, Jr.

Product Manager
Phil Garcia

The New International Version of
the Bible was used in preparing
the actvities in this book. Holy
Bible, New International Version.
Copyright ©1973, 1978, 1984 by
International Bible Society.

Publisher
Mary D. Smith, M.S. Ed.

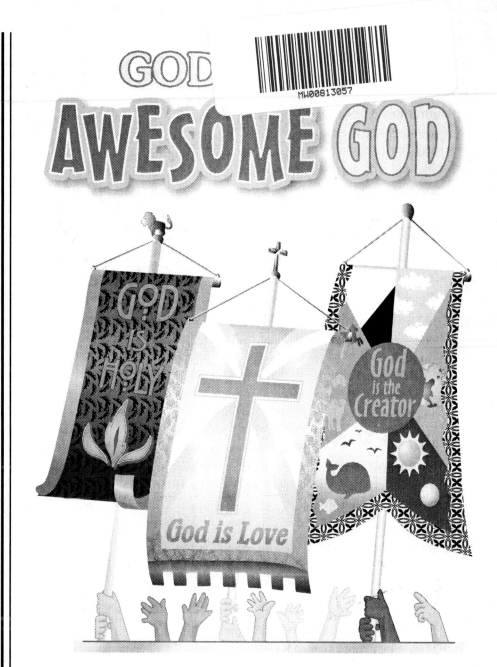

AWESOME GOD

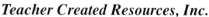

Author

Mary Tucker

Teacher Created Resources, Inc.
6421 Industry Way
Westminster, CA 92683
www.teachercreated.com

ISBN 13: 978-0-7439-7105-8

©2002 Teacher Created Resources, Inc.
Reprinted, 2007
Made in U.S.A.

Table of Contents

How do your children describe God? What is their concept of Him? Do they think of Him as a kind friend or are they somewhat frightened of His power? Most children, and many adults, have a very limited view of our unlimited God. How important it is that we help children understand that God is truly awesome!

The familiar Bible stories and creative activities in this book will help them discover for themselves that the more they learn about God, the more they still have to learn. They will find out that God is the great Creator of everything, holy and just, all-powerful and all-knowing. But He is also caring and loving, concerned about them and always ready to listen when they call on Him. They can talk to Him about anything and everything. He is their provider and protector and He loves them more than any parent or friend ever could.

In this book, children will learn about God's character from Old Testament heroes, such as Noah, Abraham and Sarah, Joseph, Moses, and others. Each lesson begins with a Bible story and includes a memory verse and a bulletin board suggestion. These are followed by puzzles, games, crafts, songs, action rhymes, and a variety of other activities for the group and for individuals to get children involved in Bible discovery.

After studying these lessons, your children will never look at God the same way again. Of course, none of us can ever completely understand God, but through the lessons in this book, children will get a glimpse of His greatness and see that He truly cares for each of them. An answer key is also provided at the back of the book.

Bible Story

Focus: Creation (Based on Genesis 1)

Since this story is so familiar to most children, focus attention by drawing a different symbol on the board to illustrate each day of Creation. Copy the small symbols next to the story poem below. Read the poem until you are familiar enough with it to say it by memory or say it with occasional glances at the printed words.

In the beginning God made the world.

But all around it empty darkness swirled.

So one day God said, "Let there be light."

There was light for the day and dark for the night.

The second thing God decided to do

Was to make the sky. Do you think it was blue?

Then the day after that He created the seas,

And the land with its flowers and grass and trees.

The next day God made some lights for the sky—

The sun and the moon and stars shining on high.

Then God made creatures to live in the sea—

Whales and dolphins and fish swimming free!

He also made birds that loved to sing

And fly through the air on feathery wings.

Then he made animals of every sort—

Ones that would roar and whinny and snort.

Others were growling and howling so loud,

While the fish swished their tails and the peacock looked proud.

Then God created the very first man,

And a woman to help him fulfill God's great plan.

Almighty God, great Creator above,

Made people special, with wisdom and love.

Why are we more special than the rest of Creation?

'Cause we're made in His image! That's God's explanation!

Verse and Bulletin Board

Memory Verse: "You are worthy, our Lord and God, to receive glory and honor and power, for you created all things." (Revelation 4:11a)

Discuss the immensity of God, the creator of all things. Briefly point out facts about the solar system, the planets, the sun 93 million miles away from the earth, etc. Talk about how God not only created the world, but also created a perfect working system to keep everything going according to His plan, such as the seasons, the rotation of the earth, etc. Let students share information they have learned about the world. Then ask them how we should respond to all that God has done. They will probably say we should praise Him and thank Him. Remind them that we should praise God, not just for what He has done for us, but also for who He is. Print the memory verse on the board. Ask some questions about it to help students understand its meaning:

- To whom are we talking in this verse? *(Underline "You" and "our Lord and God.")*

- What do we mean when we say God is worthy? *(Circle "worthy" and explain that it means God deserves something.)*

- What does God deserve from us? *(Circle "glory and honor and power.")*

- What do those words mean? *("Glory" means worship and praise; "honor" means respect and reverence; "power" means authority or rule, first place.)*

- Why does God deserve this from us? *(Draw two lines under "for you created all things.")*

Divide students into three groups. Have the first group say "You are worthy, our Lord and God." Have the second group say "to receive glory and honor and power." Have the third group say "for you created all things." Say the whole verse together.

Bulletin Board: I'm Glad God Created

Cover the bottom third of a bulletin board with green paper (for the land), the top third with light blue paper (for they sky), and the middle third with medium blue paper (for the sea). Cut letters for the caption from red paper and mount them across the top of the board.

Provide students with old science and nature magazines and gardening catalogs from which they may cut their favorite heavenly bodies, plants, animals, birds, and fish. Have them mount their pictures on construction paper and write at the bottom why they're glad God created those things. Take a class photo and mount it on construction paper. Print at the bottom of it "Us." Attach the photo to the center of the board. Let children fill the rest of the board with their nature pictures. Be sure they put the pictures on the appropriate parts of the board.

Remember Him

Decode the message from Ecclesiastes 12:1. Write the decoded letters on the lines to discover what God says you should do.

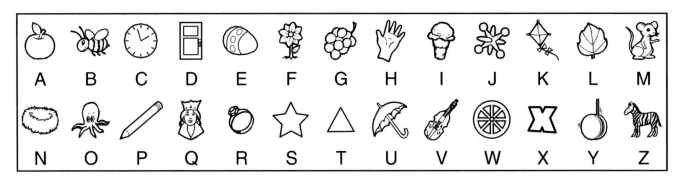

___ ___ ___ ___ ___ ___ ___ ___

___ ___ ___ ___

___ ___ ___ ___ ___ ___ ___   ___ ___

___ ___ ___   ___ ___ ___ ___   ___ ___

___ ___ ___ ___   ___ ___ ___ ___ ___.

6

Creation Star Domes

Materials

- small jars with fitting lids (such as baby food jars)
- Creation poem circle (cut from below)
- bits of plastic greenery for trees or bushes, tiny plastic animals, and people
- waterproof glue
- silver glitter
- water mixed with blue food coloring
- gummed stars
- scissors
- paint brushes

Directions

1. Let children choose bits of greenery and/or tiny animals or people to make a scene.
2. Help them glue the greenery and/or figures on the bottom of the jar lid.
3. After the glue has dried, have children fill their jars with blue water. (Mix blue food coloring in water for the whole group before they begin the project so you can get it just the right color, not too dark.)
4. Have children add some silver glitter to the water in their jars.
5. Make sure they screw the lids on their jars carefully and as tightly as possible. (Check each jar before continuing.)
6. Have them brush the glue around the jar lid so it doesn't leak.
7. Have each child cut out a Creation circle poem and glue it to the bottom of the jar (which will be the top of the dome).
8. Let children stick a few gummed stars on the jars.
9. Read the Creation poem together; then let children turn their star domes upside down or gently shake them to see the stars in the sky.

Every star that shines above, show me my Creator's love. He made this world and all that's in it, And He is with me every minute.

Creator-Sustainer

You know God is the Creator of all things. Did you know He is also the sustainer? That means He supports and maintains the world; He keeps everything going. Psalm 104 describes some of the ways God keeps the world going as it should. Look up the Bible verses to find the missing words in the sentences. Write them on the lines; then find them and circle them in the word search puzzle.

Psalm 104:5   He set the _____ on its foundations; it can never be moved.

Psalm 104:10–11   He makes springs pour _____ into the ravines; it flows between the mountains. . . . to all the beasts of the field; the wild donkeys quench their thirst.

Psalm 104:14   He makes _____ grow for the cattle, and _____ for man to cultivate—. . .

Psalm 104:16–17   The trees of the Lord are well watered, . . . There the birds make their _____.

Psalm 104:19   The moon marks off the _____, and the _____ knows when to go down.

Psalm 104:27   [All the animals] look to you to give them their _____ at the proper time.

N	Z	S	E	A	S	O	N	S	Z	Q
E	E	T	R	E	S	E	P	D	P	E
S	L	A	D	W	D	W	L	W	L	A
T	R	G	R	A	S	S	E	D	A	R
S	M	O	O	T	N	O	O	R	N	H
B	U	G	W	E	H	O	S	N	T	T
Z	K	N	E	R	F	N	R	Z	S	L

Creation Action Rhyme

Read this action rhyme and discover many of God's wonderful creations!

Bullfrogs and yappy dogs,
(Squat down and hop; then run on all fours like a dog.)

Butterflies and grunting hogs,
(Pretend to fly; then grunt like a hog.)

Elephants of enormous size
(Lumber around with one arm held down as an elephant's trunk.)

And owls that sit and just look wise,
(Stand very still with hands at side, solemnly turning your head from side to side.)

Horses with their flowing manes,
(Gallop like a horse.)

Wildebeests that roam the plains,
(Wander around on all fours.)

Kitty cats and swooping bats,
(Sit down and meow; then pretend to fly, swooping down.)

Big, brown rats and bothersome gnats,
*(Look around furtively while holding finger under nose like whisker;
then slap your arm as if bitten by an insect.)*

The sun and moon that give us light,
(Hold arms overhead in a circle.)

The twinkling stars that shine at night,
(Hold you your hands and "twinkle" your fingers.)

Bumblebees and apple trees,
(Pretend to fly while buzzing loudly; then stand straight and raise arms like tree limbs.)

God created all of these!
(Point to heaven.)

Then He created people, too
(Point out one another.)

To love Him and praise Him in all we do.
(Raise hands and face to heaven.)

Creation Scenes

Directions

1. Divide students into four teams. (If you don't have enough students to divide in this way, use fewer teams or have them all work together on one scene now and additional scenes when time allows. If you have a large number of students, let them suggest other scenes they can make, such as the following: space, ocean, and snow.)

2. Assign each team one of the following scenes to make: desert, prairie, mountains, jungle.

3. Provide a variety of craft materials and items from which students can choose to create their scenes. Begin by giving each team a large, shallow pan, such as a cookie sheet or a shallow box. (For an option, cut down the sides on a regular box.) Lay the materials out on a table. Include scissors, construction paper, glue, colored markers, paints and paintbrushes, clay, colored yarn, artificial flowers and greenery, which can be cut apart, as well as containers of sand, soil, rocks of various sizes, sticks and twigs, grass, pine cones, etc. If possible, also provide some small plastic figures of animals of various kinds and people.

4. Cover tables at which children are working with newspaper or plastic. Provide aprons or old shirts (donated by parents) for children to wear to protect their good clothes.

5. As students work on their scenes, talk about the variety of God's Creation. God could have made the earth the same everywhere, but instead He created many different kinds of landscapes, including unique plants and animals specially designed to thrive in each place. What use would mountain goats be in the desert? Their feet were made for rocky heights. And how would monkeys get along on the prairie with no trees to climb?

6. When the scenes are finished, point out that God is a Creator who deals with details. Hold up a seashell. Let students examine it as you talk. The tiniest shells in the sea are beautifully designed just for the tiny creatures that live in them. Pass around a bird feather. Show students how the feather is carefully constructed to keep out rain, yet be lightweight to provide just what a bird needs to fly. Show and discuss the marvels of some other natural items, such as dandelions, pine cones, flowers, etc.

End your discussion by thanking God for creating all things, for making them interesting and beautiful. Encourage children to express their thanks to God in their own words.

Why Me?

Read the following verses from Psalm 8. The word *man* in this passage means people like you. Follow the directions for marking these verses to understand what they tell us about God.

"When I consider your heavens,

the work of your fingers,

the moon and the stars, which you have set in place,

what is man that you are mindful of him,

the son of man that you care for him?

You made him a little lower than the heavenly beings

and crowned him with glory and honor.

You made him ruler over the works of your hands;

you put everything under his feet:

all flocks and herds, and the beasts of the field,

the birds of the air, and the fish of the sea,

all that swim the paths of the seas.

O Lord, our Lord, how majestic is your name in all the earth!"

Psalm 8:3–9

Directions

1. Underline all the things in the verses that God created.

2. Circle the question the writer asks. Write the question in your own words. (Remember that *man* is another word for person, or you.)

3. Circle what God has done for people (you).

4. Underline with two lines the work God has given people (you).

5. Draw a box around the words we can use to praise our Creator.

6. According to these verses, what is God's most important creation?

7. The best thing God did for people (you) is not mentioned in these verses. What is it? (*Hint:* If you don't know, look up John 3:16.)

Bible Story

Focus: Noah and the Ark (Based on Genesis 6–8)

Most children are more familiar with the story of Noah and the Ark than any other Bible story except, perhaps, Jesus' birth. For that reason, involve them in the story to hold their interest. As you tell the story, act it out and encourage children to copy your actions and even make up some of their own as if they are experiencing the event for themselves.

Tell the following story: "God had created people perfect, but they sinned. As the years passed and more and more people were born, they became more and more wicked. God is perfectly holy and hates sin. He said, 'I will wipe mankind, whom I have created, from the face of the earth—men and animals, and creatures that move along the ground, and birds of the air—for I am grieved that I have made them.'

God is not only holy; He is also just and fair. Among all the people on the earth at that time, only one man was holy. His name was Noah, and he walked with God. That means he loved the Lord and obeyed Him. God gave Noah directions for building a huge boat called an ark. God was going to flood the whole earth and everyone and everything would be drowned except those on the ark. So Noah and his three sons—Shem, Ham, and Japeth—began to build the ark. *(Pretend to hammer and saw.)*

They worked and worked until the ark was finished. *(Stop, look tired, and wipe your brow.)* Then God gave Noah another job. He told Noah to bring into the ark two—a male and a female—of every living creature on the earth! They would live on the ark with Noah and his family during the flood. God brought the animals to Noah, and he and his family herded them onto the ark. *(Let some children pretend to be their favorite animals while others pretend to be Noah and his family taking them on the ark.)* Not only did Noah and his family have to put all the animals on the ark; they also had to load the ark with plenty of food for the animals and for themselves for a whole year! *(Pretend to cut down grain, fish, pick fruit and vegetables, etc., and carry it all into the ark.)*

Noah did everything just as the Lord told him to and finally, the ark was loaded and ready to go. It was a huge boat with no oars, motor, or sails. So how would Noah get it going and how would he steer it? That was something Noah did not have to worry about because God would take the ark exactly where he wanted it to go.

When it began to rain, Noah and his wife and his three sons and their wives went inside the ark. *(Pretend to go inside the ark and sit down.)* When they heard the rain pouring outside, do you think Noah was afraid? Why? When it rains all day and night, do you wish it would stop? Can you imagine how Noah and his family felt when the rain continued for 40 days and nights? Everything on the earth was flooded. The trees were covered, houses were covered, even mountains could no longer be seen! The only living things not drowned were the creatures that lived in the water and the people and animals on the ark. What do you think it was like on the ark? Was it noisy? Why? What did it smell like? What do you think Noah and his family did? Mrs. Noah and her sons' wives probably cooked meals, sewed, cleaned, and maybe helped feed the animals. Noah and his sons probably fed the animals and cleaned their stalls. What else do you think they did? *(Let children share their ideas.)* Do you think they prayed? *(Let children act out some of these things.)*

Bible Story (cont.)

Finally, the rain stopped. Of course, Noah and his family couldn't leave the ark yet because the whole earth was flooded. They had to wait until the water went down. God sent a wind over the earth to help dry things up, but it took 150 days before the water went down enough for the ark to come to rest on a mountain. It was 40 days later that Noah opened a window in the ark and let a raven (a large black bird) loose. The raven did not come back, so Noah sent out a dove. The dove could not find anyplace to land since water still covered the ground. It returned to Noah with a leaf in its beak, so Noah knew that at least the water no longer covered the trees. When Noah let the dove loose again a week later, it did not return. It must have found some ground on which to land. It was not long before the ground was dry, and God told Noah it was time for him and his family and all the animals to leave the ark. Everyone was glad to set foot on land again. *(Let children show the happiness and enthusiasm the people and animals must have felt to stand on dry ground again.)*

The first thing Noah did when he got off the ark was to build an altar and make an offering to God to thank Him for His protection and care. God was pleased with Noah's offering, and He promised never again to destroy everything with a flood. In fact, God put a beautiful rainbow in the sky as a reminder of His promise. Now when we see a rainbow, we are reminded that God is holy and just, and that He keeps His promises."

Verse and Bulletin Board

Memory Verse: "For the Lord is a God of justice. Blessed are all who wait for him!"
(Isaiah 30:18b)

Discuss what we mean when we say God is just. Because He is holy, he judges and punishes sin, but He is also merciful. He saved Noah and his family because Noah was obedient. God sent His Son to take the punishment for our sins so we could be saved. Jesus is like the ark, saving all those who come to Him. Ask students to think about what the world would be like if God did not punish sin but just let people get away with doing wrong.

Bulletin Board: God Is Holy

Cover the board with blue paper. Cut a mountain from gray paper and mount it on the board. Let children use dark blue markers to draw waves on the blue paper so it looks like water, almost to the top of the mountain. Color and cut out the ark on page 15. Attach it to the top of the mountain. Cut letters for the caption from purple paper and mount them at the top of the board. Print the verse from Psalm 99:9 on the blue paper or on another sheet of paper and mount it on the board. Explain that "exalt" means to praise God. Then praise Him together.

God Is Holy

Exalt the Lord our God and worship at his holy mountain, for the Lord our God is holy.

Psalm 99:9

Ark Decorative Hanging

Students will enjoy making this Noah's Ark hanging to keep in their rooms as a reminder that God is holy and wants to save us.

Materials

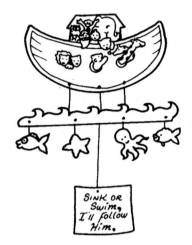

- 2 copies of the Noah's Ark pattern (page 15)
- scissors
- crayons or colored markers
- thread or fishing line
- cotton or tissue paper
- stapler and staples
- construction paper
- something with which to punch small holes

Directions

1. Color and cut two copies of the Noah's Ark pattern on page 15.
2. Put the patterns back-to-back and staple them together around the edges, leaving the top open.
3. Stuff the stapled ark with cotton or tissue paper (not too much) to give it dimension.
4. Staple the top of the ark closed.
5. Punch a couple of small holes in the bottom of the ark.
6. Put a piece of thread or fishing line, each the same length, in each hole.
7. Draw some waves on a sheet of blue paper or color them on white paper. Make two of them exactly alike.
8. Cut out the waves. Staple them together as you did the ark, leaving the top open.
9. Stuff the waves with cotton or tissue paper, then staple them closed.
10. Punch two holes in the top of the waves and connect them to the ark with the thread or fishing line.
11. Punch 3 or 4 small holes in the bottom of the waves and attach thread or fishing line of various lengths.
12. Draw some fish and other sea creatures, two of each exactly alike, and cut them out.
13. Staple the fish and sea creatures as you did the ark and waves.
14. Stuff them with cotton or tissue paper; then staple them closed.
15. Punch a small hole in the top of each and connect it to a line coming from the waves.
16. Punch another small hole in the bottom center of the ark and attach a long line to it.
17. Print one of the following slogans on a circle or square of paper, on both sides. Punch a small hole in the top, and attach it to the line connected to the ark.
    - Sink or swim, I'll follow Him.
    - God is holy and just, and He wants me to trust.
    - God saves me from the storm.

Noah's Ark Pattern

A Mini-Book About God

Directions

1. Copy the small pages below and on page 17 for each student.

2. Have students cut the pages apart; then put them in order and staple them together on the left side in a mini-book.

3. Read the pages together.

4. Have students follow the directions to complete the pages.

5. Provide construction paper so students can make covers for their mini-books.

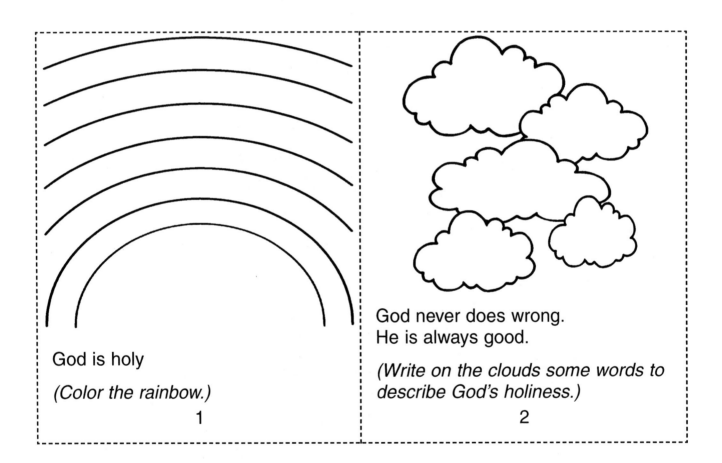

God is holy

(Color the rainbow.)

1

God never does wrong.
He is always good.

(Write on the clouds some words to describe God's holiness.)

2

A Mini-Book About God (cont.)

He is completely pure and perfect.

(Circle a number on this page to show how pure God is—1 is the lowest; 10 is the highest.)

3

God is just.
He must punish sin.

(List some sins you have done in your life. Did you deserve to be punished?)

4

I am not holy or perfect, but God loves me.

(Draw a heart. Write in it your thank-you to God for loving you.)

5

God sent Jesus to take the punishment for my sins.

(Draw a cross. Write your name on it if God has forgiven your sin.)

6

Statements About God

The following statements describe God. Choose the correct words from the box to complete the statements. Look up the verses in your Bible if you need help.

wicked	righteous	perfect	upright	evil
partiality	loving	true	holy	detests
just	justice	injustice	wrong	righteousness

1. "I am the Lord your God; consecrate yourselves and be _____,

   because I am holy." (Leviticus 11:44a)

2. "He is the Rock, his works are _____, and all his ways are

   _____. A faithful God who does no wrong, _____

   and just is he." (Deuteronomy 32:4)

3. ". . . with the Lord our God there is no _____ or

   _____ or bribery." (2 Chronicles 19:7b)

4. "Far be it from God to do _____, from the Almighty to do

   _____." (Job 34:10b)

5. "He will judge the world in _____; he will govern the peoples with

   _____ ." (Psalm 9:8)

6. "The Lord is _____ in all his ways and _____

   toward all he has made." (Psalm 145:17)

7. "The Lord _____ the thoughts of the _____ . . . ."

   (Proverbs 15:26a)

8. "Just and _____ are your ways, King of the ages." (Revelation 15:3b)

Bible Story

Focus: Abraham, Sarai, and Isaac (Based on Genesis 12:5; 15:1–6; 21:1–8)
Involve some of your students in this story by conducting it as a talk show. Students who do not have reading parts can be the television audience. You will be the talk show host.

Host: Welcome to "Can You Believe It?"—the show that guarantees to surprise you! Our very special guest comes all the way from the Old Testament—Abraham!

Audience: *(applauds as Abraham walks out and sits down)*

Host: Welcome, Abraham. I know you have a fantastic story to tell. First of all, tell us about why you decided to leave your home all of a sudden.

Abraham: Well, God spoke to me and told me to leave my country, my people, and my father's household and go to the land He would show me. So I left.

Host: Now, let me get this straight. You started out on a trip and did not even know where you were going?

Abraham: That's right. I trusted God to lead me where He wanted me to go. He promised to create a great nation from me and to bless me.

Host: How old were you when you began this adventure?

Abraham: I was 75 years old. I took my wife Sarai, my nephew Lot, and all the people and possessions that were mine.

Host: Let's bring your wife Sarai out to get her perspective on this whole thing. Sarai?

Audience: *(applauds as Sarai comes out and sits down)*

Host: Sarai, how did you feel about leaving home and moving to an unknown land?

Sarai: It was fine with me. I trusted God the same as Abraham did. Of course, after we got to the land God had promised us, I got a little discouraged and wondered when God was going to keep His promise to Abraham.

Abraham: I began to wonder about that, too. God had promised to make a great nation from me, but we did not even have any children. Then God spoke to me again and promised me that Sarai and I would have a son. He told me to count the stars in the sky, which of course I could not do. He said that is how many children and grandchildren and great grandchildren I would have. And I believed Him.

Host: OK, you were 75 years old when God promised to make you a great nation. Isn't that a little old to start a family?

Abraham: Oh, it was a lot of years before Sarai and I had the son God had promised us!

Bible Story (cont.)

Sarai:	That is right. Abraham was 100 years old when Isaac was born!
Audience:	*(shocked, surprised, gasps)*
Host:	And how old were you, Sarai?
Sarai:	Oh, I was only 90! *(smiling)*
Audience:	*(applauds, stands up and whistles, shows excitement)*
Host:	Well, let's bring this miracle baby out here! Isaac!
Audience:	*(applauds as Isaac comes out and sits down)*
Host:	How did it feel having parents so old?
Isaac:	*(laughing)* Fine. They were the best parents ever. The age did not matter. What mattered was their love for God. They taught me to love and obey Him, too.
Host:	Abraham, did this experience change your view of God?
Abraham:	Yes. It made me realize that God is totally faithful. When He says He will do something, He does it! You can count on it.
Audience:	*(applauds and cheers)*

Verse and Bulletin Board

Memory Verse: "For great is His love toward us, and the faithfulness of the Lord endures forever. Praise the Lord." (Psalm 117:2)

Discuss the verse, explaining any unfamiliar words, such as "endures forever" (lasts, never ends). Then divide children into three groups to say the verse as follows:

Group 1: For great is his love toward us,
Group 2: and the faithfulness of the Lord endures forever.
Group 3: Praise the Lord.
Everyone: Psalm 117:2

Bulletin Board: Great Is Thy Faithfulness

Play a recording of the hymn "Great Is Thy Faithfulness"; then read the words and discuss them. Cover the board with white paper and let children draw musical notes and symbols all over it. Then hand out paper and crayons or markers and have children draw pictures to illustrate God's faithfulness. (The words of the hymn suggest some ideas, such as "summer and winter, springtime and harvest.") Mount the pictures all over the board. You may want to mount the hymn on the board, too.

God Doesn't Change

Sometimes we find out we cannot count on our friends. They change their minds, or they forget. We do something that makes them mad. They break promises they have made to us. That is because they are human; they are not perfect. The only one who can be totally counted on is God. Why? He does not change. We can trust Him.

Read Numbers 23:19 and 2 Timothy 2:13 and discuss them; then learn this song.

(tune: "This Old Man")

Sometimes I disobey,
But God loves me anyway.
He is faithful and I know He'll always be.
God won't change His love for me.

When I'm scared, I want to hide,
God is right there by my side.
He is faithful and I know He'll always be.
God won't change His love for me.

When I feel helpless and
I could use a helping hand,
He is faithful and I know He'll always be.
God won't change His love for me.

When my faith isn't strong,
God's Word helps lead me along.
He is faithful and I know He'll always be.
God won't change His love for me.

Faithfully Forgiving

Follow the directions to mark up the Bible verse below. You will need crayons or colored pencils.

1. Underline in red what we need to do.

2. Underline in blue what God will do for us.

3. Circle in green the two words (adjectives) that describe God.

4. Circle in orange the word (which appears twice) that shows our problem that God will take care of.

5. Rewrite the verse on the lines, replacing the following words with words that mean the same thing: *confess, just, purify, unrighteousness*.

6. Memorize the verse.

> **If we confess our sins,
> he is faithful and just
> and will forgive us our sins
> and purify us from
> all unrighteousness.**
>
> **1 John 1:9**

_____

_____

_____

_____

_____

_____

_____

_____

Faithful Is

Do you understand what it means to be faithful? Read the words below that mean the same thing as faithful. Then fit them into the crossword puzzle. Some letters are already in the puzzle to help you.

true	reliable	trustworthy	honest
loyal	steadfast	dependable	unchanging

Do you think all these words describe God?

_____

_____

_____

_____

_____

_____

"Count-On-Him" Wheel

Use this activity to help children understand that they can count on God in any situation. They can trust Him because he will be faithful every day in every way!

Directions

1. Copy the circles on page 24 and page 25 for each student.

2. Have students color the circle below, then cut it out. Make sure they carefully cut out the triangular window.

3. Then have them cut out the circle on page 25.

4. Show them how to put the smaller circle on top of the larger one and secure them together with a brad fastener.

5. Students can move the bottom circle to read each verse through the window on the front circle.

"Count-On-Him" Wheel (cont.)

Use with directions on page 24.

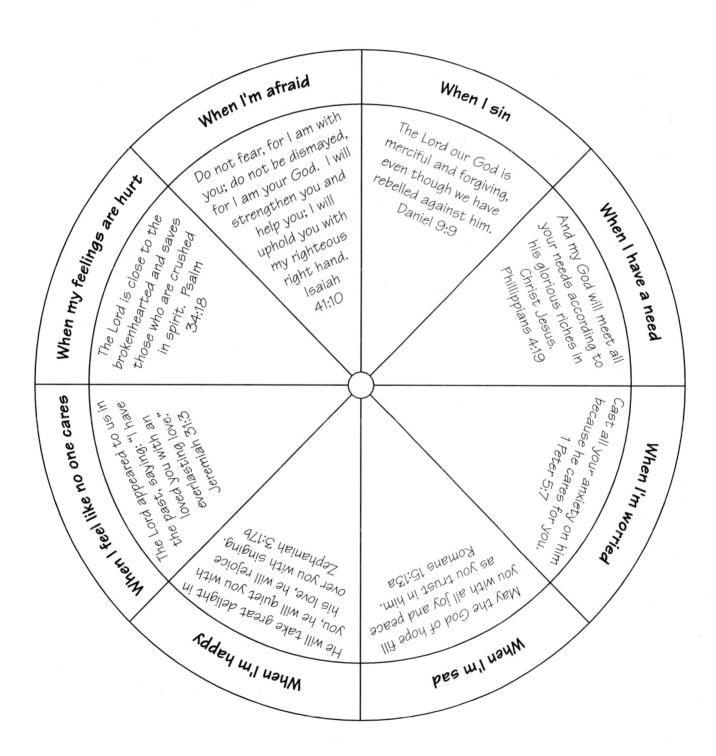

When I'm afraid — Do not fear, for I am with you; do not be dismayed, for I am your God. I will strengthen you and help you; I will uphold you with my righteous right hand. Isaiah 41:10

When I sin — The Lord our God is merciful and forgiving, even though we have rebelled against him. Daniel 9:9

When I have a need — And my God will meet all your needs according to his glorious riches in Christ Jesus. Philippians 4:19

When I'm worried — Cast all your anxiety on him because he cares for you. 1 Peter 5:7

When I'm sad — May the God of hope fill you with all joy and peace as you trust in him. Romans 15:13a

When I'm happy — He will take great delight in you, he will quiet you with his love, he will rejoice over you with singing. Zephaniah 3:17b

When I feel like no one cares — The Lord appeared to us in the past, saying: "I have loved you with an everlasting love." Jeremiah 31:3

When my feelings are hurt — The Lord is close to the brokenhearted and saves those who are crushed in spirit. Psalm 34:18

Bible Story

Focus: Joseph in Egypt (based on Genesis 37; 39–45)

Tell the following story: "Joseph was his dad's favorite son, which did not make him popular with his brothers. One day Joseph's dad gave him a beautiful, colorful robe to show how much he loved him. That made Joseph's brothers even more jealous. Sometime after that, Joseph's dad sent him to check on his brothers who had taken the family sheep to a grassy area better for grazing than the land near home. When the brothers saw Joseph coming, they began complaining about him and plotting against him. Someone even suggested killing him! Reuben, the oldest brother, talked the others into capturing Joseph alive and throwing him in a dry well. He planned to come back later when the others weren't around and rescue Joseph.

Things didn't go quite the way Reuben planned. The brothers grabbed Joseph, tore off his beautiful robe, and threw him in the well. Then they calmly sat down to eat. While they were eating, a caravan of traders came by on their way to Egypt. The brothers decided to sell Joseph to the traders. Reuben wasn't around to stop them, so Joseph was sold and taken away. When Reuben returned and heard what had happened, he said, 'What am I going to do now?' He didn't want to have to tell his father that his favorite son had been sold by his own brothers. The brothers killed a goat and dipped Joseph's robe in its blood. Then they took the bloody robe back to their father. He looked at it and immediately thought a wild animal had killed Joseph and left nothing but his robe.

But Joseph, of course, was not dead. He was a slave in the house of Potiphar, one of Pharaoh's (the king's) officials in Egypt. Instead of feeling sorry for himself, Joseph tried to make the best of the situation and serve the Lord there in Egypt. Potiphar saw that God was with him and that he was a good worker, so he trusted Joseph with more and more responsibility. Finally, he put Joseph in charge of his whole household, and God blessed Potiphar because of Joseph. Potiphar's wife was a wicked woman and when Joseph would not do what she wanted, she told lies about him. Potiphar believed her and had Joseph thrown into prison—poor Joseph.

However, even in prison Joseph was faithful to the Lord and did his best without complaining. God continued to care for Joseph, making the prison warden favor him. Soon Joseph had been put in charge of all the prisoners. The warden trusted him so much, he didn't even check on what Joseph did. The Lord was with Joseph and blessed everything he did. One day Pharaoh's cupbearer and his baker were thrown into prison. Each one had a dream that God helped Joseph explain. The cupbearer's dream meant he was going to be released from prison and get his job back. However, the baker's dream meant he was going to be executed. Joseph asked the cupbearer to speak to Pharaoh for him when he got his job back. Both things happened exactly as Joseph said.

The cupbearer forgot about Joseph until two years later when Pharaoh had two strange dreams. When no one could tell him what the dreams meant, the cupbearer thought of Joseph.

The cupbearer told Pharaoh how Joseph had explained his dream in prison. Joseph was sent for and, sure enough, was able to explain Pharaoh's dreams. They told of seven years of extraordinary crops that Egypt would have followed by seven years of famine. Joseph warned Pharaoh to look for a wise man to prepare for the famine by storing up plenty of extra grain during the years of good crops. 'Since God has made all this known to you, there is no one so discerning and wise as you,' Pharaoh said to Joseph. And the Pharaoh put Joseph in charge!

(Continued on the next page.)

Bible Story (cont.)

Joseph had storehouses built and grain stored in them so Egypt would be able to get through the coming famine. He honored God and gave God credit for everything he was able to do. When the famine began, Egypt was ready but other countries were not prepared. Famine was happening all over the world, including Israel, Joseph's home. When his father heard there was extra grain to be bought in Egypt, he sent ten of his sons to go buy grain so his family would not starve. He kept his youngest son Benjamin at home. The brothers went to Egypt to buy grain. They were sent to the person in charge—Joseph, their own brother. He had changed so much over the years, the brothers didn't recognize him. But he knew them immediately. He gave them grain and sent them home, but he kept one brother to make sure they would return, next time with their youngest brother. They didn't know what to think when they later looked in their grain sacks and discovered their money had been returned.

When Joseph's family had eaten all the grain and needed more, they went back to Egypt, this time taking their youngest brother as Joseph had said they must do. Joseph had a meal with them, then sent them away with sacks of grain. He hid his own silver cup in his youngest brother's sack. When it was discovered by one of Joseph's servants, the brothers all went back, afraid of what was going to happen to them. They were amazed when Joseph told them who he was! He lovingly forgave them for the way they had treated them, saying 'It was not you who sent me here, but God.' Pharaoh welcomed Joseph's brothers, their father, and all their families were brought to Egypt to live happily for the rest of their lives."

Verse and Bulletin Board

Memory Verse: "**The Lord is good, a refuge in times of trouble. He cares for those who trust in him.**" **(Nahum 1:7)**

Talk about the meaning of this verse. Then sing the chorus "God is so good," letting students add some verses of their own about God caring for us.

Bulletin Board: The Lord Is My Caring Shepherd

1. Cover the board with light green paper.
2. Cut letters from the caption "The Lord Is My Caring Shepherd" from dark green paper and mount them at the top of the board.
3. Enlarge the patterns on page 28 to make the shepherd and one sheep for each student in your class.
4. Color the shepherd figure and mount it on the board.
5. Talk about how the Lord cares for us. Then let each child write on a sheep one way the Lord has cared for him or her.
6. Have them attach their sheep on the board around the shepherd.
7. Print Psalm 23:1 on a paper strip and mount it at the bottom of the board.

The Lord Is My Caring Shepherd

"The Lord is my shepherd, I shall not be in want." Psalm 23:1

Shepherd and Sheep Patterns

The Shepherd's Care

Shepherd and Sheep Pantomime

1. Give each child a copy of the shepherd and sheep figures (page 28) on poster board or tagboard.

2. Have them color and cut out the figures to make puppets.

3. Show them how to cut out two strips of heavier cardboard, fold them, and glue one end of each strip to the back of the shepherd and the sheep figures for handles.

4. Let everyone work together to create background scenes based on Psalm 23 on mural paper. The scenes should include green pastures, a quiet stream, a valley between two mountains, and others that are not mentioned but implied, such as an area with wild animals like wolves or bears.

5. When the mural is completed, mount it on a wall just above a table.

6. Read Psalm 23 together and talk about the different ways the shepherd cares for his sheep—providing food and water, guiding them in right paths, watching over them in scary places, protecting them from wild animals, pouring oil on their heads to protect them from insect bites and heal sores.

7. Then read the Psalm aloud slowly, and let students pantomime the shepherd's care for the sheep with their puppets on the table in front of the background mural. You may have to read the Psalm more than once and let students take turns if there are too many of them to be at the table at one time.

Discussion

- After everyone has had a chance to take part in the pantomime, explain that Psalm 23 was written by David, who was a shepherd when he was a boy.

- Ask students who the shepherd is in David's psalm. *(God)*

- Ask them to compare how God takes care of us with how the shepherd takes care of his sheep.

- Talk about not only how God is like a shepherd, but also how people are like sheep. *(Sometimes we get confused and lost, we get tired and sick, we're stubborn, we make mistakes, we go along with the flock or crowd and may get into trouble, etc.)*

An excellent reference book is *A Shepherd Looks at Psalm 23* by W. Phillip Keller published by Zondervan Publishing House. There is also a children's version of this book which your students will enjoy.

Caring How?

What does the Bible mean when it says God is always caring for His children? Print the matching numbered letters on the numbered lines to discover some ways God is caring for you.

E 1	L 2	B 3	Z 4	A 5	F 6	M 7	D 8	I 9	O 10	G 11	S 12	U 13
Q 14	W 15	Y 16	K 17	T 18	R 19	P 20	C 21	V 22	N 23	H 24	X 25	J 26

___ ___ ___ ___ ___ ___ ___ ___
15   5   18   21   24   9   23   11

___ ___ ___ ___ ___ ___ ___
11   13   9   8   9   23   11

___ ___ ___ ___ ___ ___ ___
24   1   2   20   9   23   11

___ ___ ___ ___ ___ ___ ___ ___ ___ ___
20   19   10   18   1   21   18   9   23   11

___ ___ ___ ___ ___ ___
2   10   22   9   23   11

Psalms of Caring

Read these verses from Psalms to see how the Lord takes care of you.

> For he will command his angels concerning you
> to guard you in all your ways;
> they will lift you up in their hands, so that
> you will not strike your foot against a stone.
> (Psalm 91:11–12)
>
> My help comes from the Lord,
> the Maker of heaven and earth.
> He will not let your foot slip—
> he who watches over you will not slumber;
> indeed, he who watches over Israel
> will neither slumber nor sleep.
> The Lord will keep you from all harm—
> he will watch over your life;
> the Lord will watch over your coming and going
> both now and forevermore.
> (Psalm 121:2–4, 7–8)

Discussion

- Does God care about the little details of your life or just the big events?
- How do you know He is caring for you all the time?
- Is God able to take good care of you? Why?
- How does it make you feel to know that God cares for you this much?

Cartoon Strip

On another piece of paper draw a cartoon strip story (like you would see in the funny papers) to show what you have learned from these Psalms.

Chicken Love

Read the following story and then complete the art activity on page 33.

"Trey and Annie were excited to be visiting their grandparents on the farm. They loved living in their city apartment, but it was always nice to come to the country to see the animals and ride on the tractor with Gramps and, of course, eat Gram's homemade cookies.

As soon as the car stopped, the two city kids hopped out and raced for the big, red barn. Gramps had said there were new kittens in there somewhere. Gram and Gramps laughed, carrying the children's suitcases into the house. 'I guess we'll see them when they get hungry,' said Gram.

Later in the day the two children, hot and sweaty with dirt on their hands and clothes, came into the kitchen hoping Gram might have a snack for them. She gave them each a glass of milk and some sugar cookies shaped like cows. Trey gobbled his down and went to find Gramps, but Annie ate slowly, enjoying the food and the chance to visit with Gram.

'Did you discover the new chicks yet?' Gram asked.

'No,' said Annie with her eyebrows raised. 'Can I go see them now?'

'You'd better let me take you to see them in the morning,' Gram said. 'We have to be careful because the mother hen is a bit protective of them.'

'You mean she might peck me?' asked Annie.

'Maybe; maybe not. But it's best to be careful. There's no way for her to know you wouldn't harm them.'

The next morning Annie and Gram went to gather the eggs and feed the chickens. Gram pointed out the fluffy, yellow chicks clustered near a fat, brown hen. The hen was watching them closely. Her beak looked sharp, so Annie decided just to look, not touch.

'She's a good mother,' said Gram. Suddenly, it began to rain and the chicks all ran toward the hen. She raised her wings slightly as the chicks gathered underneath. Under her wings they were safe from the rain. 'The other day I looked out when I heard her clucking loudly. I saw her chicks running to hide under her wings. Then I looked up and saw a hawk circling in the sky. Hawks love to eat baby chicks. But her chicks were safe. It reminded me of God and us,' Gram said with a smile.

'What do you mean?' Annie asked. 'What does a chicken's love for her chicks have to do with God?'

'Let's go inside and get my Bible and I'll show you,' Gram said. When Annie brought the Bible, Gram turned to Psalm 91 and read: 'He will cover you with his feathers, and under his wings you will find refuge.'

'Wow!' said Annie. 'That's a neat picture. I'll remember it the next time I'm scared or upset and want to run away and hide. I'll run to the Lord and let Him take care of me. Thanks, Gram!'"

God's Care Stand-up Plaque

Read the story on page 32 and then complete the activity below.

1. Color and cut out the chicken.

2. Cut around the wing, leaving it connected on the left side where the broken line is. (Younger children will need help with this.)

3. Find a piece of cardboard approximately 5" x 8". (*Note*: Half of an old greeting card works well.)

4. Glue the hen to the top half of the cardboard. Trim off any parts of the cardboard that stick out beyond the hen. Be sure not to glue the wing to the cardboard. Gluing the area around the wing is okay.

5. Glue the Bible verse card behind the wing.

6. Glue bits of straw or hay around and under the hen for a nest. (You may prefer to use cut-up strips of brown paper bag for the nest.)

7. Fold up the bottom of the cardboard to make a stand. The easiest way to do this is to fold the cardboard up twice so that it has a triangular shape.

8. Encourage children to take their stand-up plaque as a reminder of God's care.

> **"He will cover you with his feathers, and under his wings you will find refuge."**
> **(Psalm 91:4)**

Bible Story

Focus: Moses and the Plagues in Egypt (based on Exodus 7–12)

As you tell the Bible story, draw the symbols (shown on the right-hand side of the page) on the board or on a large sheet of poster board.

"God had chosen Moses to go to Egypt to help free His people from slavery. He appointed Moses' brother Aaron to help him, and the two of them went to see the Pharaoh. Aaron, following God's instructions, threw his staff down in front of Pharaoh. Suddenly, the staff became a hissing snake! Pharaoh wasn't impressed. Somehow his magicians could do the same thing. But to show that God was more powerful, Aaron's snake swallowed the magician's snakes!

The next day, God told Moses to go out by the River Nile where Pharaoh was and tell him, 'Let my people go!' If Pharaoh didn't obey, the water in the river would turn to blood. When Pharaoh refused, Aaron held up his staff and the river turned to blood. The fish in the river died and people could no longer drink the water. Again, Pharaoh was not impressed because his magicians could somehow do the same thing. He turned and went into his palace.

A week later, Moses warned Pharaoh that if he did not obey God, Egypt would be plagued with frogs. Pharaoh refused and suddenly there were frogs everywhere—in people's beds, in their ovens, even crawling over people! This got Pharaoh's attention, and he said he would agree to do what God said if Moses would get rid of the frogs. Moses got rid of the frogs, but then Pharaoh changed his mind. His heart was hardened against God.

Then God caused huge swarms of gnats to appear over the land. They crawled over people and animals and bit them. Pharaoh's magicians warned him that this was the finger of God. But he wouldn't listen.

After that, God sent flies all over the land, everywhere except where the Hebrews (Israelites) lived. Pharaoh promised he would obey God and free His people if Moses would make the flies go away. But when Moses did, Pharaoh again changed his mind.

Next, God sent a plague on the livestock (horses, donkeys, camels, cows, sheep, and goats) of the Egyptians. They got sick and died, but the livestock of the Hebrews were fine. However, Pharaoh still wouldn't let God's people go.

Then the Lord plagued the Egyptian people and their animals with painful boils on their bodies. Even that didn't make Pharaoh give in. He refused to obey God.

(Continued on the next page.)

Bible Story *(cont.)*

Moses warned Pharaoh that God was so powerful He could wipe all of Egypt off the face of the earth. But He hadn't. However, God was going to send the worst hailstorm Egypt had ever had. He warned people to stay inside and keep their livestock inside. Some Egyptians believed and obeyed, so their people and animals were unharmed. But those who ignored Moses' warning suffered greatly. No hail fell in the area where the Hebrews lived. But the hail ruined the crops, killed people and animals, and stripped the trees in the rest of the land. Pharaoh promised to obey God if Moses would stop the hailstorm. But when Moses did, Pharaoh again refused to obey.

Next, God sent locusts that covered the ground and ate every growing thing that was left after the hailstorm. Pharaoh said he would obey God if Moses got rid of the locusts, but changed his mind again when the problem was gone.

Then God brought darkness to cover the land of Egypt for three days, except where the Hebrews lived. Still Pharaoh would not obey God.

Finally, God sent the worst plague of all. Moses warned that the firstborn son of every Egyptian family would die if Pharaoh did not do what God said. Pharaoh refused. That night it happened just as God had said. Even Pharaoh's firstborn son died. Every Egyptian family in the land had someone who died. And finally Pharaoh's hardened heart responded. He told Moses to take the Hebrews and leave. Many Egyptians even gave the Hebrews gold and silver and clothes to help them on their way. In a steady stream, God's people began walking away from their slavery in Egypt."

Verse and Bulletin Board

Memory Verse: "O Lord, God of our fathers, are you not the God who is in heaven? You rule over all the kingdoms of the nations. Power and might are in your hand, and no one can withstand you." (2 Chronicles 20:6)

Who is more powerful than God? (*No one*) Why? (*He created everything.*) Is God as powerful today as He was when He brought the plagues on Egypt?

Print the words and phrases of the verse on separate word cards and challenge children to put them in order.

Bulletin Board: Our Powerful God

1. Cover the board with black paper.
2. Cut letters for the caption "Our Powerful God" from gold or silver paper and mount it at the top of the board.

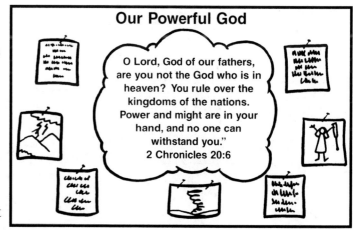

Our Powerful God

O Lord, God of our fathers, are you not the God who is in heaven? You rule over the kingdoms of the nations. Power and might are in your hand, and no one can withstand you."
2 Chronicles 20:6

3. Print the memory verse on a cloud and put it at the center of the board. As you work, play a recording of the song "Our God Is an Awesome God." Sing the chorus together.

Displays of Power

After God used His power to convince Pharaoh to let His people go, He used His power to lead and care for them. Unscramble the words to complete the sentences that tell about some of the ways the people saw God's power displayed. Look up the Bible verses if you need help.

1. When Pharaoh and his soldiers trapped God's people on the wrong side of

   the Red Sea, God _____ the waters so they could go
   _____D E D I V I D_____

   across on _____ ground. (Exodus 14:21–22)
   ____R D Y____

2. Before God gave Moses His Ten Commandments for the people, He

   displayed His power in _____ and _____
   _____D E R T U H N_____   _____N I N G L G I T H_____

   and a thick cloud over a mountain. (Exodus 19:16)

3. When the people complained about how the Lord was treating them, He

   sent down _____ and burned up part of their camp.
   ____R F I E____

   (Numbers 11:1)

4. When the people were thirsty, God produced water from a

   _____. (Numbers 20:11)
   ____C K R O____

5. When God had something to say to Balaam, He made a

   _____ talk to get Balaam's attention! (Numbers 22:28)
   ____D Y K O N E____

Who Was It?

Some well-known Bible people saw God use His power in unusual ways to help them. Match each person with the way God used His power in his or her life. Print the correct letter in front of each number. To check your answers, look up the Bible stories.

_____ 1. Jonah (Jonah 1–2)

A. God helped him use a slingshot to defeat a giant.

_____ 2. Daniel (Daniel 6)

B. God made her give birth to a son when she was 90 years old!

_____ 3. Noah (Genesis 6)

C. God made a huge fish swallow him, then release him alive.

_____ 4. Elisha (2 Kings 4:8–37)

D. God shut the mouths of hungry lions so they wouldn't eat him.

_____ 5. Joshua (Joshua 10)

E. Using a big boat, God saved him and his family from drowning.

_____ 6. David (1 Samuel 17)

F. God made the sun stand still to help him win a battle.

_____ 7. Sarah (Genesis 21)

G. God used him to bring life back to a dead boy.

Can you think of other Bible people who saw God's power in unusual ways in their lives?

How Powerful?

Look at the words below. They describe our powerful God. Find and circle the words in the word search puzzle. Then write the uncircled letters on the lines below the puzzle to find out how powerful God really is.

GREAT	FORCEFUL	MIGHTY
ABLE	STRONG	INTENSE

```
F  O  R  C  E  F  U  L
M  F  O  R  N  O  T  H
I  I  S  T  R  O  N  G
G  N  A  G  I  S  I  R
H  M  P  B  O  S  S  E
T  I  B  L  L  E  W  A
Y  I  T  H  G  E  O  T
D  I  N  T  E  N  S  E
```

___ ___ ___ ___   ___ ___ ___ ___ ___ ___ ___ ___

___ ___ ___ ___ ___ ___ ___ ___

___ ___ ___ ___   ___ ___ ___ .

(Luke 1:37)

Power Song

Sing the words below to the tune of "I've Got the Joy, Joy, Joy, Joy Down in My Heart."

God is all powerful and there is nothing He cannot do!

Nothing at all!

Nothing at all!

God is all powerful and there is nothing He cannot do,

Nothing He cannot do!

God is all powerful and He can help me do anything!

Do anything!

Do anything!

God is all powerful and He can help me do anything.

Do anything at all!

Discussion

Talk about how God's power compares with other powers.

- Is He more powerful than a hurricane? an earthquake? armies with weapons? powerful people such as presidents and kings?

- Is God more powerful than Satan? Read 1 John 4:4. Explain that those who have accepted Jesus as their Savior have God in their lives, and His power is far greater than Satan, who tries to control the world. Then read Philippians 4:13. Remind students that the all-powerful God will give them the strength they need to do what He wants. They don't have to be afraid of Satan or other people or anything!

Have students suggest specific things God can help them do. Then sing the song again, replacing the words "do anything" in the second verse with some of those ideas. Look at the example below.

God is all powerful and He can help me do the right thing!

Do the right thing!

Do the right thing!

God is all powerful and He can help me do the right thing!

Do the right thing for Him!

Power Verse Standup

Students will enjoy making this stand-up rocket to display some important Bible verses about God's power. As you hand out the rocket patterns, talk about the power it takes to get a rocket off the ground. Ask the students if they think God has as much power as a rocket. Point out that God is all powerful which means that He has more power than anyone or anything!

Materials

- rocket pattern and Bible verse strip (page 41)
- poster board or tagboard
- crayons and markers
- colored paper

- scissors
- tape
- toilet paper rolls cut in half

Directions

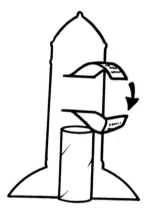

1. Copy the rocket pattern on poster board or tagboard for each student. Copy the Bible verse strip on colored paper.

2. Let students color the rocket. Then they may cut out the rocket and the Bible verse strip.

3. Help them cut two slits near the top of the rocket where the lines are.

4. Show them how to slip the Bible verse strip through the bottom slit (from the back), then through the top slit so that one of the Bible verses is showing.

5. Have them tape the ends of the Bible verse strip together to make a loop.

6. Give each student half a toilet paper roll.

7. Help them tape the toilet paper roll to the back of the rocket for a stand.

8. Have students turn the Bible verse strip so they can read each verse about God's power.

9. Encourage students to take the rocket home and memorize each verse.

Power Verse Stand-up Patterns

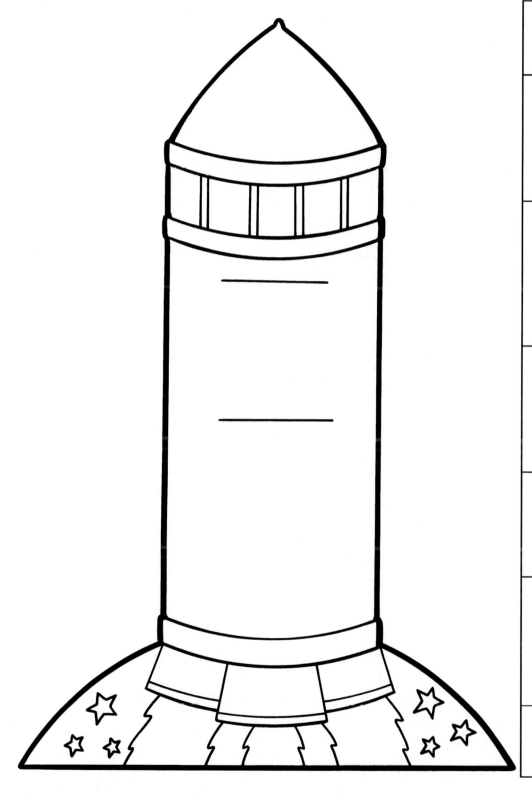

Tape to other end.

"The Lord is my strength and my shield; my heart trusts in Him, and I am helped. . . ."
Psalm 28:7

"The name of the Lord is a strong tower; the righteous run to it and are safe."
Proverbs 18:10

". . .the one who is in you is greater than the one who is in the world."
1 John 4:4

"For nothing is impossible with God."
Luke 1:37

". . .be strong in the Lord and in His mighty power."
Ephesians 6:10

Tape to other end.

Bible Story

Focus: Samuel's Birth (based on 1 Samuel 1)

As you read this Bible story poem, let students pantomime some of the actions.

Hanna couldn't eat; Hanna couldn't sleep.

Hanna was so sad, all she could do was weep.

She wanted a child, but she had none,

So Hanna asked God to give her a son.

At the tabernacle Hanna knelt down.

She cried and she prayed, but she didn't make a sound.

"Give me a son," she said, "and if You do,

I'll be sure to give the boy back to You.

He'll serve You, Lord, all of his days.

I'll teach him to follow in Your ways."

Eli the priest saw Hanna praying.

He saw her lips move but couldn't hear what she was saying.

He didn't realize she was in such deep distress.

He thought she was drunk, and that she should confess.

"I've been praying," Hanna told the priest Eli.

"I was silent so only God would hear my cry."

"May God give you what you prayed for,"

Eli said to Hanna as she walked out the door.

Hanna went home and slept and ate.

She'd given God her problem and now she would wait.

She trusted the Lord; her worrying was done.

And the Lord answered Hanna's prayer with a son.

She names him Samuel, her own little boy.

And she thanked God for hearing her and giving her such joy.

She loved and taught her son and covered him with prayer.

Then she took him to Eli, to live with him there.

Samuel grew up to be a priest for the Lord,

Because God answered prayer and a woman kept her word.

Verse and Bulletin Board

Memory Verse: "I call on you, O God, for you will answer me; . . . ." (Psalm 17:6a)
Ask students how often they pray and how God answers their prayers. Encourage them to share answered prayer experiences.

- Does God always answer our prayers by giving us what we ask for, as He did with Hanna? Why not?

- Do we sometimes ask Him for things we don't really need?

Help children understand that God knows what is best. If we ask for something that is not in His plan, He won't give us the answer we want. We need to trust Him to do what is best for us, even if we don't understand it right now. And our prayers should be more than just asking God for things. We should also pray to praise Him for who He is, to thank Him for what He has done for us, and just to tell Him we love Him.

Teach students the following song to the tune of the chorus of "B-I-N-G-O."

> I c-a-l-l, I c-a-l-l, I c-a-l-l
>
> I call on You, O God.
>
> For You will answer me, You will answer me, You will answer me.
>
> You'll answer when I call.

Bulletin Board: I Can Talk to God

1. Cover the board with light blue paper.

2. Cut the letters for the caption "I Can Talk to God" from dark blue paper and attach them at the top of the board.

3. Enlarge the praying child figure from page 44.

4. Color it and mount it at the bottom center of the board.

5. Cut speech balloon shapes from white paper.

6. Give one to each child to write a prayer on (a request, praise, thanks, etc.).

7. Attach the prayers around the praying child.

8. Then cut out letters for the bottom caption "I Know He Will Answer" from red paper and mount them under the child.

9. When the board is finished, take time to have the children read their prayers aloud to God or say new prayers to Him. Then sing the memory verse song together.

Praying Child Pattern

Pray Anywhere, Anytime

God wants you to talk to Him; it doesn't matter where or when. He is always ready to listen to you. The Bible is filled with stories of people praying. Match each prayer with the correct person and place or time. If you need help, look up the Bible verse.

_____ 1. ". . .Salvation comes from the Lord."

A. David in a field with his sheep (Psalm 23:4)

_____ 2. ". . .O God, please strengthen me just once more. . ."

B. Jesus on the cross (Luke 23:34)

_____ 3. ". . .I will fear no evil, for you are with me; . . ."

C. Job when he lost his wealth and his children (Job 1:21b)

_____ 4. "So give your servant a discerning (wise) heart. . ."

D. Samson being held captive in the Philistine temple (Judges 16:27–28)

_____ 5. ". . .The Lord gave and the Lord has taken away; may the name of the Lord be praised."

E. Jonah in the belly of a whale (Jonah 2:9b)

_____ 6. "Father, forgive them, for they do not know what they are doing."

F. Solomon when he became king (1 King 3:9a)

To find out how God answered their prayers, look up the stories of these people in the Bible books listed.

Prayer Journal

Your students will enjoy having their own prayer journal in which to jot down prayer requests, prayers, God's answers to prayer, and important things to remember about prayer.

1. Reduce the figure of the praying child on page 44 so it fits easily on half a sheet of paper (5 ½" x 8 ½"). Give a copy of the figure to each child to color, cut out, and glue on a half sheet of paper. They may print "My Prayer Journal" on the figure.

2. Give each student three or four sheets of 8 ½" x 11" paper to cut in half.

3. Copy the bottom half of this page for each student.

4. Have students assemble their pages together with the praying child figure on the cover, the bottom half of this page as the second page, and the empty pages following. Staple the pages together into a journal for each child.

5. Discuss the best way to use the prayer journal. Explain that a journal is a good way to remember prayer requests and to make a note of when and how God answers each prayer. (Younger children will need help from a family member to do this.)

6. Go through the bottom half of this page. Encourage students to use it as a pattern for the rest of their journal pages.

7. Periodically, ask volunteers to share some of the contents of their prayer journals.

What God Has Taught Me About Prayer:

Answers to Prayer:

Prayer Requests:

The God Who Answers

Mount Carmel was crowded with people who had come to see an unusual contest. The prophets of the idol Baal prepared an offering to be burnt on an altar. Then they spent a whole day calling on their god to send fire to burn up the offering. Hours went by and the prophets of Baal called on their idol until they were hoarse, but nothing happened. Baal did not answer them. "The god who answers by fire," Elijah had said, "he is God." And everyone had agreed. Now everyone knew Baal was not the true God.

Then it was Elijah's turn. He prepared an offering and laid it on the altar over some wood. Then he had four large jars of water poured on the offering once, twice, three times. The offering and the wood were soaked and the trench around the altar was filled with water. Then Elijah prayed, "Answer me, O Lord, answer me, so these people will know that you, O Lord, are God. . . ." (1 Kings 18:37)

Read 1 Kings 18:38. Then complete the picture below to show what happened. Who was the one true God?

A Prayer Reminder

Directions

1. Copy the clock on heavy paper or tagboard for each student.

2. Let students color and cut out the clock.

3. Show them how to fold it on the broken line to make it stand.

4. Read the words on the clock.

5. Encourage students to keep the clock by their beds as a reminder to pray when they wake up, when they go to bed, and at other times during the day.

Bible Story

Focus: David and Goliath (based on 1 Samuel 17)

Let students copy your actions as you read and act out the Bible story rhyme below and on page 50.

David was a shepherd boy whose faith in God was strong.
(Point to heaven.)
One day his dad gave him some food and said, "Now run along,
(Pretend to take packages in your arms.)
And take this food to King Saul's camp where your brothers are."
(Point off in the distance.)
So David left his flock and started off; it wasn't far.
(Walk in place, carrying packages.)
When David reached the battle lines, he went to greet his brothers.
(Wave to imaginary brothers.)
Just then he heard a shout that frightened them and all the others.
(Look startled and turn around.)
It was Goliath, nine feet tall, with armor and a spear.
(Look way up as if at a giant.)
He challenged Israel's army while they all quaked with fear.
(Shake with fear.)
"If one of you will fight me and kill me if you can,
(Stand tall, poke out chest, and point to yourself proudly.)
We Philistines will serve you, every single man."
(Point to yourself, then to imaginary people one by one.)
David was astonished that all the Israelites
(Look surprised and shocked.)
Were so scared of the giant they had run away in fright!
(Run in place with arm over head in fright.)
"I'll fight him!" David told the king. "You're just a boy!" said Saul.
(Point to yourself.)
"I killed a lion and a bear," said David standing tall.
(Stand tall with feet apart and hands on hips.)
"God helped me protect my sheep and took my fear away.
(Raise fist.)
And the Lord who gave me strength back then will strengthen me today."
(Point to heaven.)
So Saul gave David armor and put a helmet on his head.
(Put on imaginary armor and helmet.)
But David took them off again. "I don't need these," he said.
(Take off imaginary armor and helmet and shake head "no.")
He took his sling in his hand and picked up five smooth stones,
(Hold imaginary sling and pretend to pick up stones.)

Bible Story *(cont.)*

Then without spear or armor, David went to fight alone.
(Walk in place slowly.)
"What is this?" Goliath laughed when he saw the boy.
(Stand tall and look down, pointing down.)
He decided this would be a fight he would enjoy!
(Put hands on hips, lean back, and laugh heartily.)
"Today," said David, "everyone will know that God is Lord!
(Reach out arms toward heaven.)
He will help me win this fight without spear or sword."
(Point to yourself, then hold out arms one at a time.)
Toward Goliath David ran. He was calm and ready.
(Run in place.)
He put a stone into his sling and slung it quick and steady.
(Pretend to put stone in sling and swing it over your head.)
The stone went right where David aimed and smacked the giant's head.
(Smack yourself in the forehead.)
The ground shook as he fell down. The Philistine was dead!
(Fall down.)

Verse and Bulletin Board

Memory Verse: "...for he guards the course of the just and protects the way of his faithful ones." **(Proverbs 2:8)**

Explain that David's son, Solomon, wrote these words, perhaps while thinking of his father's fight with Goliath. Discuss whom the Lord guards and protects: the "just" and "his faithful ones" (those who love and serve Him). Sing the verse to the tune of "God Is So Good" to learn it. (You'll need to say "and protects the way" quickly in the third line.)

Bulletin Board: God Can Smash Giant Problems!

1. Cover the board with yellow paper.
2. Cut letters for the caption "God Can Smash Giant Problems!" from black paper and mount them across the top of the board.
3. Trace around a large hammer, cut it out, and attach it to the board.
4. Give each child a piece of paper on which to write a problem or fear he or she has.
5. Discuss how God protects us by helping us conquer our giant problems as He helped David conquer the giant Goliath.

God Can Smash Giant Problems!

6. Have them crumple their papers and put them on the board to look like "smashed" problems.
7. Pray together, asking God to smash the problems. After prayer, discuss other ways God protects us.

Where Will You Go?

When you're afraid, where will you go for protection? How can you have confidence to face trouble? Find your way through the maze to the only one who can help you every time. Then read what David wrote in Psalm 62:5–8. Do you agree with him?

Fear Buster Mini-Book

Directions

1. Copy the bottom half of this page and page 53 for each student.

2. Have them cut the pages apart on the broken lines and assemble the cover and five mini-pages together in order.

3. Staple the pages together to make a mini-book.

4. Then have students go through their books, following the directions on each page. You may want to go through the pages together as a group, especially with younger children. If some of your students have trouble with reading, print the Bible verses and cut them out for them to glue on the correct pages.

5. When the books are completed, encourage students to take them home and keep them handy to refer to whenever they are afraid and need to be reminded of God, their protector.

Fear Busters!

Reminders of God's Power To Protect Me

_____

(my name)

Psalm 91:11 reminds you that God uses His angels to protect you.

(Draw an angel in the box.)

1

Fear Buster Mini-book *(cont.)*

Say this verse: "My flesh and my heart may fail, but God is the strength of my heart. . . ." (Psalm 73:26) Is that true?

(Draw a picture in the box to show what scares you the most.)

2

God says He will hear and answer when you ask Him to help you.

(Write your prayer for protection in the cloud.)

3

_____ said He would be with me wherever I may go.

And He _____ breaks a promise; this is true I know.

So when I'm feeling all alone and scared, I'll say a _____.

I know I can count on Him because He's always there!

(Complete the poem with the missing words.)

4

For I am convinced that
neither death nor life,
neither angels nor demons,
neither the present nor the future,
nor any powers,
neither height nor depth,
nor anything else in all creation,
will be able to separate us from
the love of God that is in
Christ Jesus our Lord.
Romans 8:38–39

God protects you because He loves you.

(Read the verses above. Circle the things that can separate you from God's love. Underline the things that cannot.)

5

David and Goliath Activities

A Stone's Throw Action Scene

1. Copy the picture on page 55 on heavy paper for each student to color.
2. Then help students punch two small holes in the scene where the back dots appear.
3. Provide string for students to poke through one hole and out the other, then tie it in the back. The string will stretch from David's sling to the giant's head.
4. Help students glue a grain of rice, an unpopped popcorn kernel, or a tiny piece of gravel to the string at the front of the picture. Wait for the glue to dry completely.
5. Then show students how to manipulate the string in the back to put the stone in David's sling, and move it to hit the giant in the forehead.
6. Sing the following song together and let students "sling" the stone as they sing about David's victory.

David's Victory Song

Teach students this song so they can sing it as they work their action scenes. Sing the words to the tune of "If You're Happy and You Know It."

> I put a stone inside my little sling,
> And then I gave my sling a mighty fling.
> By the Lord my stone was led
> Right to the giant's head.
> Now praise and thanks to God is
> what I sing!

An Equal Fight?

Discuss the apparent inequality of the fight between David and Goliath.

- What weapons did Goliath have? List them on the board as students mention them. *(a bronze javelin and a pointed spear that weighed 600 shekels)*
- What was Goliath's armor like? *(a bronze helmet, a coat of bronze armor weighing 5000 shekels, bronze leg armor, he also had someone else carrying his shield, which was probably huge.)*
- How big was Goliath? *(over nine feet tall)*
- What weapons did David have? *(a sling and a pouch containing five stones)*
- What was David's armor like? *(He didn't wear any armor.)*
- How big was David? *(He was not a full-grown adult yet, so he was possibly between 5 and 5 1/2 feet tall.)*
- Was it an equal fight? *(Let students discuss it briefly.)* Goliath wasn't worried because he thought he had all the power on his side, but he was wrong.
- What power did David have on his side? *(God)*
- After God helped David defeat the giant, how did the Israelite army react? *(They suddenly became brave and chased after the Philistines who were running away.)*

Print this sentence on the board: "Little is much when God is in it." Ask students to explain how this statement relates to David's fight with Goliath.

"Do not be afraid of them; the Lord your God himself will fight for you." (Deuteronomy 3:22)

Protection Acrostic

Why does God protect and care for you? Look up the Bible verses and find the missing words in the sentences. Print the words on the lines of the acrostic. Then read the letters in the boxes.

1. God is our _____ _____. (Psalm 32:7)

2. We can take _____ in God. (Psalm 16:1)

3. David could _____ in peace because God was keeping him safe. (Psalm 4:8)

4. God promises to protect the just _____. (Psalm 37:28)

5. Our God is a God who _____. (Psalm 68:20)

6. Don't be afraid, because God will be with you _____ you go. (Joshua 1:9)

7. David said that God was his _____. (2 Samuel 22:3)

8. David prayed, "When I am afraid, I will trust in _____." (Psalm 56:3)

9. God is an ever-present help in _____. (Psalm 46:1)

10. The Lord cares for those who _____ in Him. (Nahum 1:7)

1. ___ ☐ ___ ___ ___ ___ ___   ___ ___ ___ ___ ___

2. ___ ☐ ___ ___ ___ ___

3. ___ ☐ ___ ___ ___

4. ___ ☐ ___ ___ ___ ___

5. ___ ___ ☐ ___ ___ ___

6. ___ ___ ☐ ___ ___ ___ ___ ___

7. ___ ☐ ___ ___ ___ ___

8. ___ ☐ ___ ___

9. ___ ___ ___ ☐ ___ ___ ___ ___ ___

10. ___ ___ ___ ☐ ___ ___ ___ ___

Bible Story

Focus: Elijah Fed by Ravens (based on 1 Kings 17)
Choose students who are good readers to help you present the Bible story as a TV news report. You be the news anchor.

News Anchor: This is W-BBL, and this is the morning news. Our top news story continues to be about the weather. Let's go to our meteorologist for an up-to-the-minute report.

Meteorologist: Well, the good news is, if you're planning a picnic this week, you won't have to worry about being rained out. The bad news is the drought continues over most of the land. Israel has been especially hard hit. There's not been a drop of rain for over a year! Farmers have lost most of their crops, cattle have died, and water has become almost as precious as gold! King Ahab is furious. No one really knows how much longer this drought will continue.

News Anchor: It's true that the king is angry. He blames Elijah, a prophet of God, for the terrible conditions in Israel. A year ago Elijah visited Ahab in his palace and gave him a message from God. He said, "There will be no dew or rain in the next few years until I say so!" And it wasn't long after that when the rains stopped coming. Where is Elijah now and what is he doing? Here's a special report on the prophet from reporter Aaron Ben Guran.

Reporter: I am in the town of Zarephath with Elijah who has agreed to talk with us. After you gave God's message to King Ahab, you just disappeared from sight. Where did you go, Elijah?

Elijah: The Lord told me to go down to the Kerith Ravine, east of the Jordan River, and camp out by the brook. He took care of me there for a long time.

Reporter: How did God provide for you?

Elijah: It was really a miracle. He sent ravens, big black birds, to bring me food every morning and evening, and I drank water from the brook. When the brook finally dried up because of the drought, God told me to come here to Zarephath where a widow would provide me with food.

Reporter: And here is that widow and her son. Ben, come over here and talk with us for a couple of minutes. Has your mother told you what happened the day she met Elijah?

Son: Yes. My mother was gathering sticks for a fire when Elijah called to her near the gate of the city. He asked her to bring him a drink of water and she agreed. Then he asked if he could also have a piece of bread. Mom explained that she had only enough flour and oil to make a last meal for the two of us. She was sure we would die after that.

Reporter: So Elijah didn't get his bread?

Son: Well, yes, he did. He promised my mother that if she would make bread for him, as well as for the two of us, God would reward her by seeing that our flour and oil would not be used up. She did it, and we are still using the flour and oil that God keeps providing!

(Continued on the next page.)

Bible Story (cont.)

Reporter: Thanks, Ben. Now we'd like to hear from your mother. How did you feel about Elijah when this happened, Ma'am?

Widow: I was amazed at the power of his God and thankful to Him for helping us. But later I became very angry at Elijah.

Elijah: You see, her son got sick and died. She blamed me. I carried the boy up to my room and laid him on my bed. Then I asked God to give the boy back his life, and He did. I took the woman's son back down to her and said, "Look, your son is alive!"

Widow: I was thrilled, of course. And I saw clearly that Elijah is a man of God, the true God. I believed in Him.

Reporter: Thanks so much for sharing your stories with us. Now back to the news desk.

News Anchor: Thanks for that interesting report on God's provision. That's the news for today. Stay tuned to W-BBL for up-to-the-minute news and weather. Have a good day!

Verse and Bulletin Board

Memory Verse: "The Lord is gracious and compassionate. He provides food for those who fear him." (Psalm 111:4b–5a)

Ask students what else God provides besides food. List the items on the board. Paraphrase the verses to help students understand them: "The Lord is kind. He gives food to those who love and respect Him." Say the verses together several times, each time replacing the word "food" with one of the other items on the board that God provides.

Bulletin Board: God Provides for All

1. Cover the bottom half of the board with green paper and the top half with blue paper.

2. Cut letters for the caption "God Provides for All" from red paper.

3. Mount them at the center of the board.

4. Have students cover the green part with flowers they have drawn and cut out of gardening catalogs, as well as artificial flowers.

5. Add a word card: "Lilies of the Field."

6. Let them draw and cut birds from magazines and attach them to the blue part.

7. Add a word card: "Birds of the Air."

8. Then have students draw themselves, label the pictures "ME," and scatter them around the board.

What Does God Give Us?

Can you find some of the things God gives us in the word search puzzle? Find the words listed below in the word search puzzle and circle them. Then write the leftover letters on the lines below the puzzle to find out how much God really gives us. Look up 1 Timothy 6:17 to check your answers.

food   **shelter**   **family**   **pets**

home   **clothes**   **friends**

```
F   A   M   I   L   Y   E   H
V   E   R   Y   T   H   I   O
F   R   I   E   N   D   S   M
S   H   E   L   T   E   R   E
F   C   L   O   T   H   E   S
N   O   G   F   O   R   O   U
R   E   O   N   P   E   T   S
J   O   Y   D   M   E   N   T
```

GOD GIVES US

___ ___ ___ ___ ___ ___ ___ ___ ___ ___ ___

___ ___ ___ ___ ___ ___ ___ ___

___ ___ ___ ___ ___ ___ ___ ___ ___ ___ ___!

A Miracle Meal

Tell the following story to your students and then have a discussion using the questions below.

"George Muller was used to God providing his needs. God had provided the money necessary for him to buy a large house and start an orphanage, and God continued to provide what was needed to keep the orphanage going. But sometimes it seemed to George that the Lord waited until the last minute to meet his needs. Oh well, it was probably helping his faith to grow. Today wasn't all that different from other days when George had trusted God for a miracle. It was time for breakfast, but there wasn't a scrap of food to feed the children.

George had the children sit down at the tables where plates and glasses and silverware had been placed, ready for breakfast. The children sniffed, but didn't smell any food cooking. Then George asked the children to bow their heads as he thanked God for the food, even though there wasn't any!

'Father, we thank You for the food you are going to give us to eat this morning. And thank You for all You have given us in the past. Amen.'

Suddenly, there was a knock at the door. George walked to the door, opened it, and found the town baker there. 'Good morning, sir,' said the baker. 'Last night the Lord woke me up and told me I should bake some bread for you and your orphans, so I did. I have it with me.'

'Thank you, friend, but I'm afraid we have no money to pay for the bread,' George replied.

'No, no!' said the baker. 'I could not ask you to pay for bread that God asked me to bake for you!' And with that, the baker went back out to get the bread. George sent some of the children to help carry the bread inside.

A couple of minutes later one of the boys returned with his arms full of bread. 'Mr. Muller, guess what?' he said excitedly. 'While we were helping the baker get the bread, a man stopped and asked if we could use some milk. He was driving by in his milk delivery cart when one of the wheels broke! He said he needs to get rid of the milk to lighten the load, and we can have all we want!'

The orphans grinned and so did George. 'Of course, we want the milk,' he said. 'Let's go and tell the milkman.' As they hurried out the door, George said, 'Thank You, Lord. You've done it again!'"

Discussion

This is a true story. George Muller spent most of his life caring for orphans, over ten thousand of them in all. He never asked people for money, but trusted God to provide all his needs. He loved telling people how God provided, often in unusual ways.

- How did George Muller show that he trusted the Lord to provide?

- Do you think it was an accident that the milk cart broke down in front of the orphanage?

- Has God ever provided for you in an unusual way?

What Is Our Part?

God can and will provide for us. He is our great provider. But what is our part? What does God want us to do? Look at the letter puzzle below. Use a pencil or crayon to shade each box that has a letter in it from the statement: "God Can and Will!" Then read and write the word that appears.

B	E	F	Q	Z	Z	R	E	E	S	F	Z	F	B	J	T	T	M	Y
G	D	O	V	I	I	L	B	C	Y	G	Q	A	I	L	X	C	C	G
Z	A	F	F	C	Z	C	Q	N	Z	L	S	G	T	T	B	Y	A	T
M	D	E	E	A	N	X	R	A	R	C	T	C	L	C	Q	M	L	S
Y	N	Q	B	G	H	G	Y	N	P	I	R	M	V	G	R	R	D	Q
B	W	M	B	D	E	A	E	G	G	W	S	L	L	A	Z	B	G	E
Q	R	F	Y	B	Q	E	E	S	S	Q	Z	X	H	U	U	V	F	H

Read the first part of Proverbs 3:5 and fill in the blanks below.

"____ ____ ____ ____ ____ in the Lord

with all your

____ ____ ____ ____ ____ . . ."

Stories of Provision

The Bible is filled with stories of how God provided for people. Four are pictured below. Draw a line from each picture to the Bible verses that tell the Bible story. Can you think of other Bible stories about God's provision?

Food for the Israelites

Pure water for Elisha

Genesis 22:13–14

Exodus 16:13–15

1 Kings 3:10–12

2 Kings 2:19–22

A ram for Abraham's sacrifice

Wisdom for King Solomon

Refrigerator Magnet

It's easy to take God's provision for granted. You open your refrigerator several times a day. Do you thank God for providing the food inside it each time? Make a magnet to put on your refrigerator to remind your whole family to be thankful to God for giving you food to eat and enjoy.

Materials

- frozen juice can lid or jar lid
- one of the circle patterns on this page
- scissors
- crayons or markers
- glue
- clear adhesive plastic
- a small magnetic strip
- colored construction paper or felt

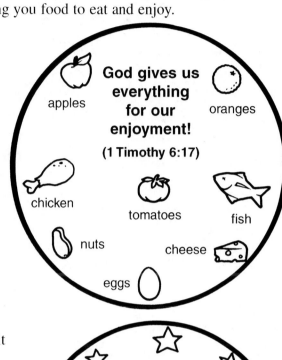

God gives us everything for our enjoyment! (1 Timothy 6:17)

apples oranges chicken tomatoes fish nuts cheese eggs

Directions

1. Choose one of the circle patterns. Color it and cut it out.

2. Glue the circle pattern to the top of the jar lid. (If your lid is larger than the circle pattern you choose, you will need to trace around the lid on colored construction paper or felt. Glue the circle pattern you colored on top of it. The background circle will provide a border.)

3. Trace around the lid on clear adhesive plastic.

4. Cut out the plastic circle and carefully put it over the colored circle. Smooth out any bubbles and creases in the plastic.

5. Glue a small magnetic strip on the back of the lid.

6. When the glue has dried, take the reminder magnet home and put it on your refrigerator.

Remember To Thank God!

He fills our house, especially the refrigerator, with good things. (based on Job 22:18)

Thank You, God, For all You provide— For this refrigerator And the good food Inside!

Thanking God Action Rhyme

Have students make up their own actions to act out this rhyme. Read it slowly so they will have time to do all their actions.

What do I have to thank God for?

What has He given me?

Food, water, clothes to wear,

A home and a family,

A brain that thinks, ears that hear,

Eyes that see everything,

A nose to smell wonderful smells,

A mouth to talk and sing,

Hands that can touch and write and hold

And clap and scratch and tickle,

Taste buds that can tell the difference between

A strawberry and a pickle.

God gave me so much to be thankful for.

He supplies my needs every day.

I want to use what He's given me

To thank Him in every way.

With my eyes and my brain I'll study His Word;

With my mouth I'll pray and sing,

And clap my hands to show Him my thanks

For providing everything!

Bible Story

Focus: Jonah and the Whale (based on Jonah 1–2)
As you tell this familiar story, act out and let children copy your actions.

"God told Jonah, 'Go to the city of Nineveh and preach my message to the sinful people there.' *(Stretch out arm and point to the right.)* But Jonah didn't want to go *(Shake head "no.")*, so he went in the opposite direction! *(Stretch out arm and point to the left.)* Jonah tried to run away from God by taking a sea voyage. He packed his bags *(Pretend to stuff clothes in a bag.)*, went down to the shipping office *(Walk in place, carrying bag.)*, paid his passage money *(Pretend to count out coins.)*, and got on a ship headed for Tarshish.

As Jonah sailed away *(Rock back and forth as if standing on a boat.)*, he was probably saying to himself, 'I'll go so far away God will never find me!' But Jonah was wrong. God knew exactly where he was. Suddenly, the ship began to rock back and forth on the sea *(Rock back and forth more violently and act as if to grab hold of something.)* as the ship sailed into a storm. The sailors were afraid the ship was going to break apart and they began throwing the cargo into the sea to lighten the load *(Pretend to throw things overboard.)*. Everyone was scared *(Look frightened.)*, everyone but Jonah that is. He was asleep below deck and didn't even realize what was happening *(Cradle your head on your hands and close your eyes as if sleeping.)*.

The ship's captain woke Jonah up *(Stretch and yawn.)* and said, 'How can you sleep? Get up and call on your God!' Meanwhile, the sailors had decided to cast lots, something like throwing dice, to see if they could find out who was responsible for the storm *(Pretend to throw dice.)*. They knew this was no ordinary storm. They decided Jonah was the one responsible for their distress.

'Who are you? Are you responsible for the trouble we're having?' they questioned Jonah. They knew they had to get some answers fast before they all drowned.

Jonah realized that his disobedience had put everyone on the ship in danger. So, he told them that he was running away. 'I worship the God of heaven who made the sea and the land,' he said *(Point toward heaven, then toward the sea and land.)*.

The sea was getting rougher and more dangerous as Jonah talked. The sailors asked him, 'What should we do for you to make the sea calm down?' Jonah told them the storm was his fault, so to stop it they must throw him into the sea *(Point to yourself, then to the sea.)*.

No one wanted to kill Jonah to save themselves, so they tried to row the ship back to land. They rowed harder and harder *(Pretend to row a boat.)*, but it was no use. The sea grew even wilder! Finally, they cried out to God and asked Him to forgive them. Then they grabbed hold of Jonah and threw him overboard *(Pretend to throw Jonah overboard.)*. The instant they did it, the sea became calm. The sailors were amazed *(Look shocked and somewhat afraid toward heaven.)*.

(Continued on the next page.)

Bible Story *(cont.)*

When the sea calmed down, Jonah must have looked around him while trying to swim *(Pretend to swim.)*. He was surely going to drown out in the middle of the sea with the ship already far away from him. What was that? Something was coming toward him! It was a huge fish. Jonah swam as hard as he could *(Pretend to swim and splash around.)*, but suddenly everything got dark. He must have thought he was drowning, but suddenly he felt something firm under his feet. He stopped swimming and looked around, but he couldn't see anything; it was too dark *(Put your hands out and look around as if trying to see in the dark.)*. Then he realized what had happened. The fish had swallowed him! *(Hold hands up to your face as if in shock.)* Had Jonah escaped drowning in the sea only to die inside a fish?

He realized that this was no ordinary fish just as the storm had been no ordinary storm. He knew God was in this. God had kept Jonah alive in spite of his disobedience. Jonah began to pray *(Bow down with your head between your hands.)*. He confessed his sin to God and praised God for saving his life. God saw Jonah inside the fish and heard his prayer. For three days and nights Jonah was inside the fish; then God had the fish throw him up on dry ground. Jonah didn't even have to swim to shore! As he lay on the beach, how do you think Jonah felt? *(Sit or lie back as if exhausted.)* He had learned one thing for sure—when God tells you what to do, you'd better do it *(Shake index finger.)*; because you can't run from God. He sees and hears and knows everything!"

Verse and Bulletin Board

Memory Verse: "His eyes are on the ways of men; he sees their every step." (Job 34:21)
Ask students to share how it makes them feel to know that God sees everything they do, hears everything they say, and even knows what they think. Point out that if we love the Lord and are living for Him in obedience, this is a comforting truth that makes use feel secure. But if we are disobeying Him, we do not like the idea of God's eyes on us. To help students memorize the verse, have them "sign" it. Let them come up with their own "signs" for words, such as pointing up for "His" and "He."

Bulletin Board: You Can't Hide from God!

1. Cover the board with blue paper.

2. Have student use dark blue markers to draw waves so it looks like water.

3. Cut letters for the caption "You Can't Hide from God!" from yellow paper and mount them at the top of the board.

4. Cut a large fish from gray paper and mount it on the board.

5. Use a dark marker to print the poem on the fish.

6. Discuss ways we sometimes try to hide from God (not praying or going to church, ignoring Him, etc.).

You Can't Hide from God!

You can't hide from God.
Even if you run far,
He knows what you're thinking;
He sees where you are.

Jonah Stick Puppets

Copy the three patterns on heavy paper for children to color and cut out. Then have them glue each one to a craft stick or tongue depressor to make a stick puppet. Sing the song on page 68 together and have children act out the story with their puppets.

Puppet Action Song

After students make stick puppets, using the patterns on page 67, have them sing this song to the tune of "B-I-N-G-O" and act out the story with their puppets.

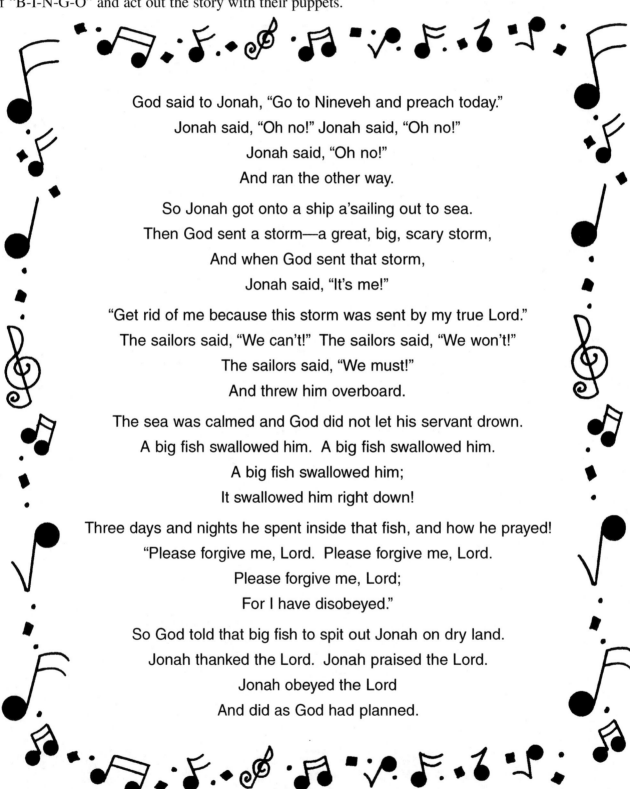

God said to Jonah, "Go to Nineveh and preach today."

Jonah said, "Oh no!" Jonah said, "Oh no!"

Jonah said, "Oh no!"

And ran the other way.

So Jonah got onto a ship a'sailing out to sea.

Then God sent a storm—a great, big, scary storm,

And when God sent that storm,

Jonah said, "It's me!"

"Get rid of me because this storm was sent by my true Lord."

The sailors said, "We can't!" The sailors said, "We won't!"

The sailors said, "We must!"

And threw him overboard.

The sea was calmed and God did not let his servant drown.

A big fish swallowed him. A big fish swallowed him.

A big fish swallowed him;

It swallowed him right down!

Three days and nights he spent inside that fish, and how he prayed!

"Please forgive me, Lord. Please forgive me, Lord.

Please forgive me, Lord;

For I have disobeyed."

So God told that big fish to spit out Jonah on dry land.

Jonah thanked the Lord. Jonah praised the Lord.

Jonah obeyed the Lord

And did as God had planned.

How God Looks at Us

David was just a boy, the youngest in his family, when God told Samuel he would be the next king of Israel. Samuel thought David's oldest brother would be a better choice. He was older and stronger, more impressive looking than the young shepherd boy. Read the words in the cloud to find out what God told Samuel.

> Do not consider his appearance or his height, for I have rejected him. The Lord does not look at the things man looks at. Man looks at the outward appearance, but the Lord looks at the heart.
> (1 Samuel 16:7)

David became Israel's greatest king and when he died, his son became king after him. Read below what David said to his son.

> And you, my son Solomon, acknowledge the God of your father, and serve him with wholehearted devotion and with a willing mind, for the Lord searches every heart and understands every motive behind the thoughts.
> (1 Chronicles 28:9a)

Directions

1. Use a red crayon or pencil to underline in the first verse what we look at in other people. What impresses us?
2. Use a blue crayon or pencil to circle in both verses what God looks at in people.
3. Use a blue crayon or pencil to underline in the second verse what God knows about us. Why does God understand people better than we do?
4. Use a green crayon or pencil to underline in the second verse what David said his son's attitude should be toward God.
5. What does it mean to serve God with "wholehearted devotion and a willing mind?"

_____

6. If that is how you want to serve Him, print your initials next to those words in the verse.

Describing God

There is no one like God; He is one of a kind. One of the words we use to describe God is "awesome." What does that word mean to you?

_____

Write some other words and sentences to describe God below. Look up the Bible verses to find some great descriptions of Him. Use some words from the Bible and some of your own.

Job 42:2   Psalm 147:4–5   Hebrews 4:13   Isaiah 55:8–9   Psalm 48:1

Awesome

God Is . . .

"God Knows Me" Craft

A few weeks before class, make the craft described below so that the grass will be growing well by the time you have students make the craft. Talk about how God is always watching us and caring for us. Then read Matthew 10:30. Students will be intrigued by the idea that God knows the number of hairs on their heads. Explain that this is just one example of how much He knows about them. Hold up the craft you made. Tell students that they will make the craft as a reminder that God is so concerned about them, He even cares about how many hairs they have on their heads! How encouraging to know that God knows and loves us that much!

Materials

- white Styrofoam cups
- colored markers or crayons
- pencils
- fast-growing grass seed
- potting soil

Directions

1. Give each student a white Styrofoam cup on which to draw facial features (eyes, nose, mouth, and ears). Encourage students to make the cup faces look as much like their own as they can. For example, if a student wears glasses, he should draw glasses on the cup face; if a student has freckles, those should be added to the cup, etc.

2. Let students fill the cup almost to the top with potting soil.

3. Have them poke holes in the soil with a sharpened pencil, place the grass seeds in the holes, then cover the holes with soil.

4. Add a little water to the cups and place them in the sunlight or let students take them home to care for them. Remind them that the seeds need to be watered often.

5. When the grass has grown fairly tall, students can use scissors to give their cup heads a haircut.

Bible Story

Focus: Prophecies of Jesus' Birth and Death (based on selected Old Testament and New Testament Books)

Discuss the following topics with your students: "What do you think is the main topic of the Bible? *(Let students share their ideas.)* The main topic of the whole Bible is Jesus Christ. The Old Testament looks forward to Jesus' birth and death. It says 'He's coming and this is what He will be like!' The New Testament says, 'He is here and this is what He did!'

The Old Testament contains many prophecies about Jesus. What is prophecy? *(telling about something that will happen in the future)* God shared the details of His Son's coming with His prophets hundreds and hundreds of years before Jesus' birth. Those men never got to see Jesus in person, but they knew a lot about Him. They knew that God was going to send His only Son to the earth to die and take the punishment for people's sin. Why would He do that? *(He loves the people He made and wants everyone to be in a right relationship with Him.)*

In the very first book of the Old Testament, Genesis, God mentioned Jesus, but not by name. After Adam and Eve sinned, God punished them, and He also punished the serpent who tempted them to sin. God said in Genesis 3:15, 'And I will put enmity between you and the woman, and between your offspring and hers; he will crush your head.' God was saying that someday Jesus would crush Satan! And that prophecy came true when Jesus died and came back to life, conquering death.

God told the Prophet Isaiah a lot about Jesus. *(Read Isaiah 7:14)* Isaiah knew that Jesus would be born to a virgin and would be called Immanuel. That was one of Jesus' names. Do you know what it means? *(God is with us)* Did that prophecy come true? *(Yes, when Jesus came to live on the earth, he was God living with people.)* God also told Isaiah how Jesus would be rejected and killed for people's sins. *(Read Isaiah 53:2–9 aloud, if possible from a children's version of the Bible.)* Did those things really happen to Jesus? *(Yes, many people hated Jesus, but He willingly gave His life for them and for all of us.)*

God told another prophet, Micah, where Jesus would be born. *(Read Micah 5:2)* Did that prophecy come true? *(Yes, God worked it out that even though Mary and Joseph lived in Nazareth, they had to go to Bethlehem so Jesus was born there.)* More than 700 years later after Jesus was born, wise men went searching for him. They stopped at the king's palace in Jerusalem to find out where He was. The king had the Jewish chief priests and teachers see if they could find out this information. They looked in the Old Testament book of Micah and were able to tell the wise men that the prophet said Jesus would be born in Bethlehem. The wise men went to Bethlehem and found Him there, just as the prophet had written.

God told the prophet Zechariah how Jesus would come into Jerusalem for His triumphal entry. *(Read Zechariah 9:9.)* Did that prophecy come true? *(Yes, that's exactly how Jesus came into Jerusalem that day.)* And the people who waited along the roadside to see Jesus shouted, 'Blessed is he who comes in the name of the Lord!' as He rode by. Those are actually words written in Psalm 118:26, talking about God's Son several hundred years before Jesus was born.

(Continued on the next page.)

Bible Story *(cont.)*

It's very clear that God had a perfect plan to send His Son into the world long before it actually happened. Because God loved us so much, He was willing to let His Son go through mistreatment and even death. That was the only way people could have their sins forgiven. And God's love was big enough to pay the price because God is love. His love is perfect and nothing can ever change it. God loves those who hate Him, who never speak His name except to swear. He loved those who killed His Son. He loves everyone. Does everyone love Him? Why? *(Let students share their ideas.)* The next time you read the Bible, remember that it is a love story—all about God's love for people and the way He showed that love."

Verse and Bulletin Board

Memory Verse: "This is how God showed his love among us: He sent his one and only Son into the world that we might live through him." (1 John 4:9)

To help students understand and memorize this Bible verse, break it into four sections:

- How?   This is how God showed his love among us.
- Who?   He sent his one and only Son
- Where? into the world
- Why?   that we might live through him

Divide students into four teams. Assign a question and the answer from the verse to each team. Have them say the verse, with the questions, in order a few times. Then have the teams trade parts and say the verse again. Do this until they can say the verse all together.

Bulletin Board: God Is Love

1. Cover the board with white paper.
2. Let students use red markers to draw hearts all over the paper or give them gummed hearts to stick all over the board.
3. Cut the letters for the caption "God Is Love" from red paper and mount them at the middle of the board.
4. Provide paper hearts on which students can write or let them trace hearts of various sizes and cut them out of pink and red paper.

5. Hand out dark-colored markers and have students write Bible verses (or selected phrases from the verses) about God's love on the hearts. (See the following Bible references: Deuteronomy 7:9; Psalm 36:5a; Psalm 52:8b; Psalm 118:1; Jeremiah 31:3; Zephaniah 3:17; John 3:16; Romans 5:8; 1 John 3:1; 4:9, 11, 16b, 19.)
6. Then they may attach the hearts all over the board.

A Poem About God's Love

Write the missing words on the lines to complete this poem about God's love.

How do I know that God is love?

The _____ tells me so.

When I read it, I discover

The truth God wants me to know.

He sent His _____ to die for me.

If that's not love, what is?

Jesus took the punishment

I deserve and made it _____.

God has shown His _____ for me

In many other ways:

Providing, protecting, and caring for me

Every single day.

_____ will never separate me

From God's love; it's true.

I don't deserve it, but He loves me,

And I love Him _____.

Responding to God's Love

We know that God loves us. How should we respond to God's love? Look up the Bible verses to find out. Write on the hearts what the verses say to do.

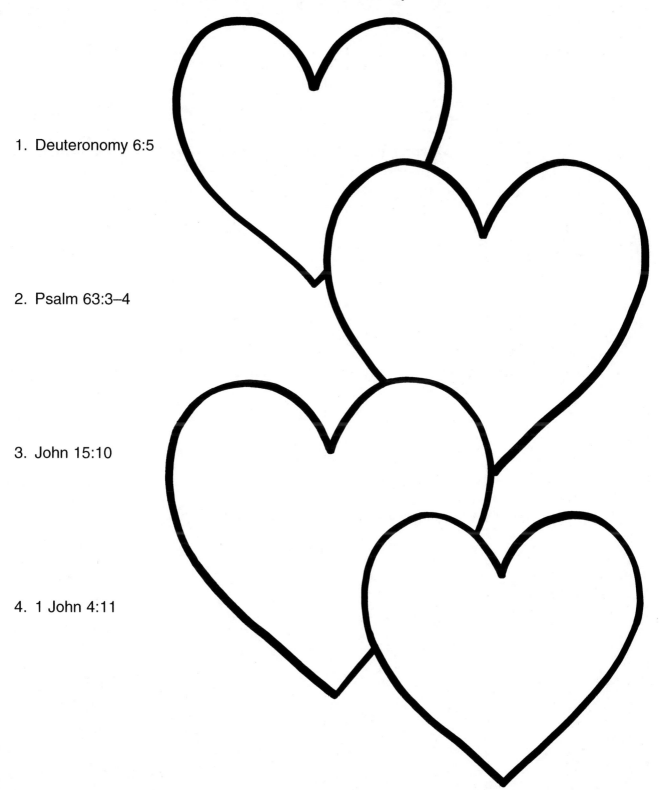

1. Deuteronomy 6:5

2. Psalm 63:3–4

3. John 15:10

4. 1 John 4:11

God's Love Bookmarks

Copy the patterns on this page for students. Let each student choose one to color, cut out, and fold in half. Then have the student glue a magnetic strip to the inside bottom of each half of the folded bookmark. When it is slipped over a page, the magnets will attract and hold the bookmark in place.

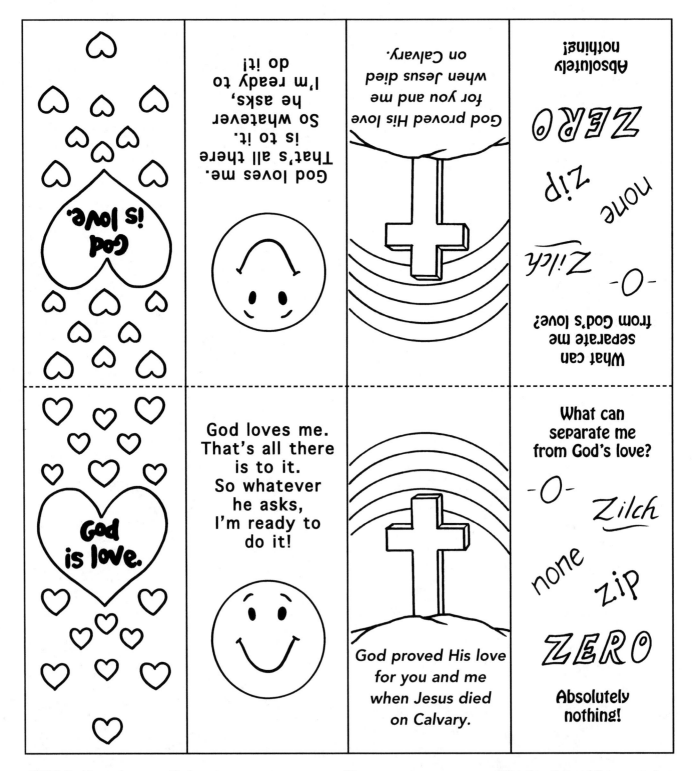

Proving God's Love Skit

Characters: Eve, Noah, Sarah, Joseph, Israelite, Hannah, David, Elijah, Jonah, Student 1, Student 2

Student 1: You're always saying that God is love, like He invented love or something. How do you know God really loves you? Can you prove it?

Student 2: There are lots of people in the Bible who experienced God's love in their own lives. They can witness of His love.

Eve: My name is Eve. I was the first woman God created. He loved Adam and me and gave us everything we could ever want. There was only one thing He told us not to do, and we did it! We disobeyed Him and He punished us, but He still loved us and cared for us our whole lives.

Noah: Noah here. Remember me? God destroyed the world because of people's wickedness, but He saved me and my family and two of each animal in the ark that He told me how to build. God is holy and He could have destroyed us too because we were not perfect, but He loved us and kept us safe.

Sarah: My name is Sarah. God promised my husband Abraham that we would have a son. We failed Him many times, but God was faithful and kept His promise. He gave us a son when I was an old woman. His love for Abraham and me did not change even though we were not always faithful to Him.

Joseph: This is Joseph. I could tell you so much about God's love! My brothers hated me when I was young and because of them I ended up in Egypt as a slave. God cared for me and blessed me in amazing ways. He even reunited me with my family. God's loving care was what got me through all my troubles.

Israelite: As an Israelite, I was a slave in Egypt with the rest of my people. God proved His love for us when he sent Moses to free us. God used His power to send plagues on the Egyptians, but not on us, that convinced Pharaoh to let us go. If it were not for God's love, I would still be a slave in Egypt.

Hannah: I'm Hannah. God showed His love for me when He answered my prayer for a son. When He was old enough I sent my son Samuel to the tabernacle to serve the Lord who gave him to me.

David: This is David, the giant killer! I wrote many psalms about God's love. He protected me by helping me kill a giant when I was just a boy. God's love never failed me.

Elijah: I am Elijah the prophet. During a drought God provided me, first through birds, then through a widow. It was His love that made Him take care of me this way.

Student 2: Those are only a few of the Bible people who could tell you about God's love. But the greatest demonstration of God's love was when He sent His son Jesus to die for the sins of people, not just those who love Him, but even those who don't. That's why I know God loves me, and you too.

Weekly Circle Calendar

Students will enjoy making this circular calendar to remind them of God's love every day of the week. Let them color the calendar and draw designs or add stickers on each day of the week. Then have them cut out the two calendar pieces and tape the pieces together end-to-end to make a circle. They can stand up the circle calendar on a desk or near their beds in their rooms to look at every day.

Monday	**Tuesday**	**Wednesday**	**Thursday**
Have a good day. And remember, I love you! God	Nothing can separate you from God's love! (Romans 8:39)	Jesus is God's proof that He loves you.	**God loves you!** ♡ **For Sure** ♡

Friday	**Saturday**	**Sunday**
	Do you wonder if anyone loves you? God does.	
For God so loved the world, that He gave His only Son. (John 3:16)		God loves you 24-7 (24 hours a day, 7 days a week).

Page 6

REMEMBER YOUR CREATOR IN THE DAYS OF YOUR YOUTH.

Page 8

earth, water, grass, plants, nests, seasons, sun, food

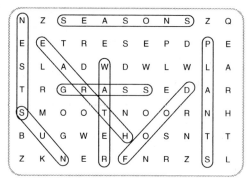

Page 11

1. heavens, moon, stars, man, flocks and herds, beasts of the field, birds of the air, fish of the sea, all that swim the paths of the sea
2. Why do you care about me?
3. "crowned him with glory and honor"
4. "You made him ruler over the works of your hands" and "you put everything under his feet"
5. "O Lord, our Lord, how majestic is your name in all the earth!"
6. man
7. He gave His only begotten Son—Jesus.

Page 18

1. holy
2. perfect, just, upright
3. injustice, partiality
4. evil, wrong
5. righteousness, justice
6. righteous, loving
7. detests, wicked
8. true

Page 22

1. confess our sins
2. will forgive us our sins and purify us from all unrighteousness
3. faithful, just
4. sins

5. If we tell our sins, he is faithful and fair and will forgive us our sins and make us free from guilt from all that is not right.

Page 23

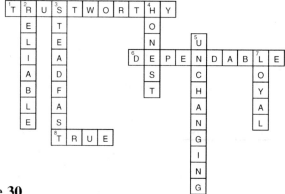

Page 30

WATCHING

GUIDING

HELPING

PROTECTING

LOVING

Page 36

1. divided, dry
2. thunder, lightning
3. fire
4. rock
5. donkey

Page 37

1. C
2. D
3. E
4. G
5. F
6. A
7. B

Page 38

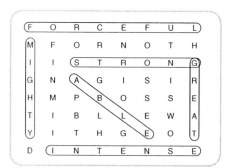

FOR NOTHING IS IMPOSSIBLE WITH GOD.

Page 45

1. E
2. D
3. A
4. F
5. C
6. B

Page 51

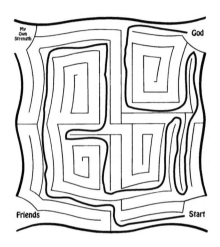

Page 56

1. h i d i n g   p l a c e
2. r e f u g e
3. s l e e p
4. f o r e v e r
5. s a v e s
6. w h e r e v e r
7. s h i e l d
8. y o u
9. t r o u b l e
10. t r u s t

Page 59

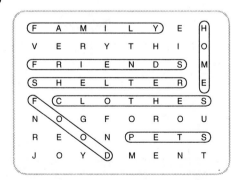

EVERYTHING FOR OUR ENJOYMENT

Page 61

TRUST

Trust, heart

Page 62

Food for the Israelites = Exodus 16:13–15

Pure water for Elisha = 2 Kings 2:19–22

A ram for Abraham's sacrifice = Genesis 22:13–14

Wisdom for King Solomon = 1 Kings 3:10–12

Page 69

1. appearance, height
2. heart
3. "the Lord searches every heart and understands every motive behind the thoughts"
4. "acknowledge the God of your father, and serve him with wholehearted devotion and with a willing mind"
5. dedicating all of one's energy or enthusiasm and having a ready or agreeing mind when serving the Lord

Page 74

Bible

Son

His

love

Nothing

too

Page 75

1. Love God with all your heart, soul, and strength.
2. Glorify and praise Him.
3. Obey His commands.
4. Love one another (other people).